SOLUTIONS MANUAL
ELEMENTS OF
ENGINEERING
PROBABILITY
&
STATISTICS

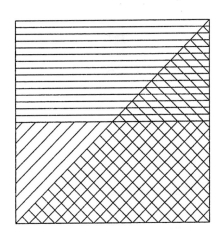

RODGER E. ZIEMER

University of Colorado
at
Colorado Springs

PRENTICE HALL Upper Saddle River, NJ, 07458

Acquisitions Editor: **Tom Robbins**
Assistant Editor: **Nancy Garcia**
Cover Designer: **Paul Gourhan**
Special Projects Manager: **Barbara A. Murray**
Production Editor: **Dawn Blayer**
Supplements Cover Manager: **Paul Gourhan**
Production Coordinator/Buyer: **Donna Sullivan**

 © 1997 by Prentice-Hall, Inc.
A Pearson Education Company
Upper Saddle River, NJ 07458

Printed in the United States of America

10 9 8 7 6 5 4 3 2 1

ISBN 0-02-431621-0

Prentice-Hall International (UK) Limited, *London*
Prentice-Hall of Australia Pty. Limited, *Sydney*
Prentice-Hall Canada, Inc., *Toronto*
Prentice-Hall Hispanoamericana, S.A., *Mexico*
Prentice-Hall of India Private Limited, *New Delhi*
Prentice-Hall of Japan, Inc., *Tokyo*
Simon & Schuster Asia Pte. Ltd., *Singapore*
Editora Prentice-Hall do Brasil, Ltda., *Rio de Janeiro*

CONTENTS

PROBLEM SOLUTIONS

CHAPTER 1
INTRODUCTION

Problem 1-1

```
%        Solution to Prob. 1-1
%
X = [3 6 8 9 9 4 4 4 0 8];
Y = [16 20 38 60 16 15 -2 24 21 25];
X_bar = mean(X);
Y_bar = mean(Y);
fprintf('The mean of X is: %f and the mean of Y is %f \n',X_bar,Y_bar)
```

» pr1_1
The mean of X is: 5.500000 and the mean of Y is 23.300000

Problem 1-2

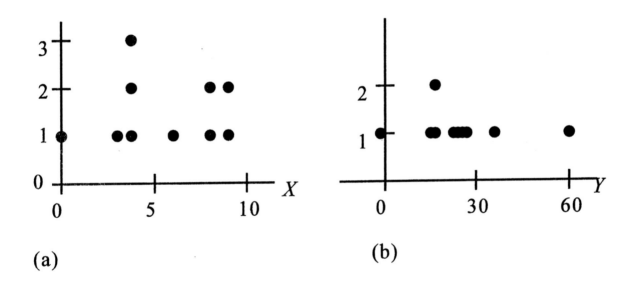

(a)   (b)

Problem 1-3

```
%        Solution to Prob. 1-3
%
X = [3 6 8 9 9 4 4 4 0 8];
Y = [16 20 38 60 16 15 -2 24 21 25];
subplot(211),hist(X, 5),grid,xlabel('Sample value'),...
        ylabel('Number of samples'),...
```

```
        title('Histogram plot for data sample X with 5 bins')
subplot(212),hist(Y, 9),grid,,xlabel('Sample value'),...
        ylabel('Number of samples'),...
        title('Histogram plot for data sample Y with 9 bins')
```

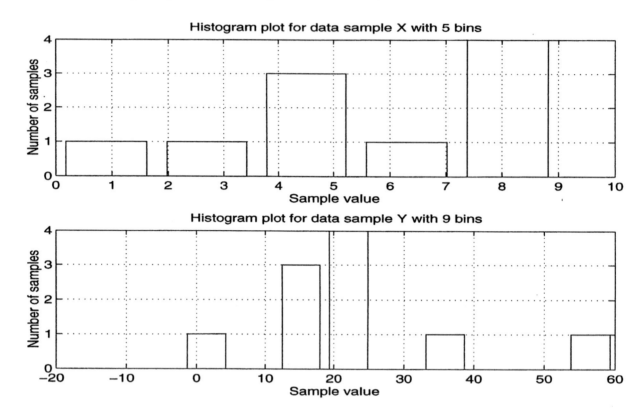

Problem 1-4

decade	unit
-10 - -1	-2
0 - 9	
10 - 19	5 6 6
20 - 29	0 1 4 5
30 - 39	8
40 - 49	
50 - 59	
60 - 69	1

CHAPTER 2
FUNDAMENTAL CONCEPTS OF PROBABILITY

Problem 2-1

(a) Personal; (b) Personal or possibly equally likely outcomes; (c) Relative frequency or possibly equally likely outcomes; (d) Relative frequency and equally likely outcomes; (e) Relative frequency.

Problem 2-2

(a) Outcomes: $\{R1, R2, \ldots, R10, W_a1, W_b1, W_a2, W_b2, \ldots, W_a10, W_b10\}$ where the subscripts "a" and "b" denote the first and second disks with the same number and color.

$$P(\text{red}) = \frac{10}{30} = \frac{1}{3}; \quad P(W3) = \frac{2}{30} = \frac{1}{15}$$

(b) Outcomes: $\{H1, H2, H3, T1, T2, T3\}$.

$$P(\text{at least one head}) = \frac{3}{6} = \frac{1}{2}$$

(c) Outcomes: $\{1 \text{ spot up}, 2 \text{ spots up}, \ldots, 6 \text{ spots up}\}$.

$$P(2 \text{ or } 3 \text{ spots up}) = \frac{2}{6} = \frac{1}{3}$$

(d) Outcomes: $\{\$100, \$200, \ldots, \$3,000\}$.

$$P(\geq \$500) = 1 - P(\$100 \text{ or } \$200 \text{ or } \$300 \text{ or } \$400) = 1 - \frac{4}{30} = \frac{13}{15}$$

Problem 2-3

(a) P(ace of spades) = 1/52; (b) P(any ace) = 4/52 = 1/13; (c) P(red ace) = P(ace of hearts or ace of diamonds) = 2/56 = 1/26; (d) P(any face card) = P(jack, queen, king, or ace, any suit) = 4×4/52 = 4/13; (e) P(any black face card) = 2×4/52 = 2/13; (f) P(any pair of aces) = P(1st ace) P(2nd ace I 1st ace)= (4/52)(3/51) = 1/(13×17) = 1/221.

Problem 2-4

(a) $P(A = \{0 \leq \Theta \leq 45^0\}) = 45/360 = 1/8$; (b) $P(B = \{22.5^0 \leq \Theta \leq 67.5^0\}) = 45/360 = 1/8$; (c) $P(A \cap B) = P(22.5^0 \leq \Theta \leq 45^0) = 1/16$; (d) $P(A \cup B) = P(0 \leq \Theta \leq 67.5^0) = 3/16$.

Problem 2-5

Let $A = A_1$ and $B = A_2 \cup A_3$. Note that $A \cap B = \emptyset$ and $A \cup B = A_1 \cup A_2 \cup A_3$. Therefore

$$P(A \cup B) = P(A_1 \cup A_2 \cup A_3)$$

$$= P(A) + P(B)$$

$$= P(A_1) + P(A_2 \cup A_3)$$

$$= P(A_1) + P(A_2) + P(A_3)$$

Use induction to prove for arbitrary n. Assume

$$P(A_1 \cup A_2 \cup \cdots \cup A_{n-1}) = \sum_{n=1}^{n-1} P(A_i)$$

Hence

$$P(\{A_1 \cup A_2 \cup \cdots \cup A_{n-1}\} \cup A_n) = \sum_{n=1}^{n-1} P(A_i) + P(A_n)) = \sum_{n=1}^{n} P(A_i)$$

Problem 2-6

(a) $A \cup B = \{1, 3, 5, 7, 9\} \cup \{0, 2, 4, 6, 8\} = \{0, 1, 2, 3, 4, 5, 6, 7, 8\}$; (b) $A \cup B \cup C = S$; (c) $A \cup B \cup C \cup D = S$; (d) $A \cup B \cup C \cap D = S \cap D = D$; (e) $A \cap B = \emptyset$; (f) $A \cap D = \{3, 5\}$; (g) $(A \cup B) \cap (C \cup D) = \{0, 1, 2, 3, 4, 5, 6, 7, 8, 9\} \cap \{3, 4, 5, 6, 10\} = \{3, 4, 5, 6\} = D$; (h) $A \cap B \cup C = \{1, 3, 5, 9\} \cap \{0, 2, 4, 6, 8, 10\} = \emptyset$.

Problem 2-7

$$\bar{A} = \{0, 2, 4, 6, 8, 10\}; \quad \bar{B} = \{1, 3, 5, 7, 9, 10\};$$

$$\bar{C} = \{0, 1, 2, 3, 4, 5, 6, 7, 8, 9\}; \quad \bar{D} = \{1, 2, 7, 8, 9, 10\}$$

Problem 2-8

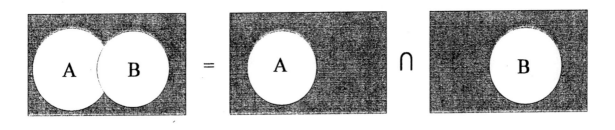

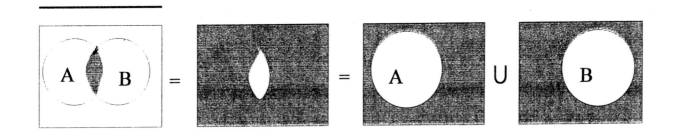

The top set of figures illustrates

$$\overline{A \cup B} = \bar{A} \cap \bar{B}$$

The bottom set of figures illustrates

$$\overline{A \cap B} = \bar{A} \cup \bar{B}$$

5

Problem 2-9

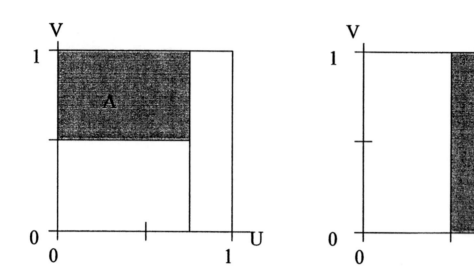

(a) $P(A) = 3/4 \times 1/2 = 3/8$; (b) $P(A) = 1/2$; (c) $P(A \cup B) = 3/4$ (obvious from a sketch of $A \cup B$; (d) $P(A \cap B) = 1/8$ (obvious from a sketch of the overlap area between A and B.

Problem 2-10

(a) $P(X) = (113 + 57 + 202)/1372 = 372/1372$; (b) $P(B) = (57 + 116 + 175)/1372 = 348/1372$; (c) $P(A \cap X) = 57/1372$; (d) $P(B \cup X) = (372 + 348 - 57)/1372 = 663/1372$;

Problem 2-11

A Venn diagram is shown on the next page. From this diagram, it follows that:

    (a)   Number of persons reading 1 paper only = 10000 + 30000 + 5000 - 2000 - 8000 - 4000 + 1000 = 32,000;

    (b)   Number of persons reading at least two newspapers = 2000 + 4000 + 8000 - 1000 - 1000 = 12,000;

    (c)   Number of persons reading no newspapers = 100,000 - [10,000 + 30,000 + 5,000] = 55,000.

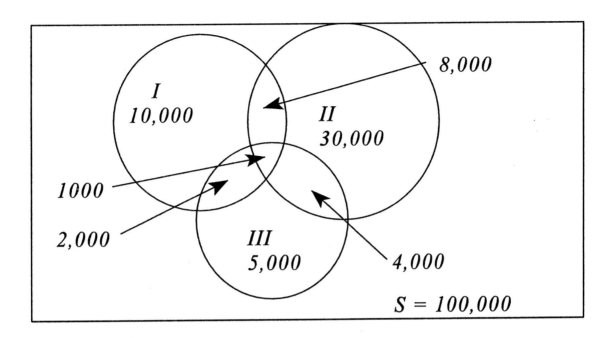

Problem 2-12

To work this problem consider the Venn diagrams shown below for parts (a), (b), and (c).

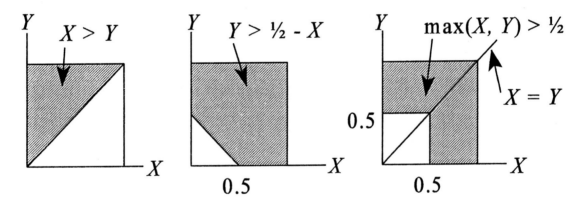

(a) From the first figure, it is obvious that $P(X > Y) = 1/2$; (b) From the middle figure, we deduce that
$P(X + Y > 1/2) = 1 - 1/8 = 7/8$; (c) From the last figure, it follows that $P(\max(X, Y) > 1/2) = 1 - 1/4 = 3/4$; (d) this is the area within the square of side 1 and under the parabola $xy = 0.25$, or 0.597.

Problem 2-13

(a) From a Venn diagram, it follows that $B = (B \cap A^c) \cup (A \cap B)$ and the two sets in parentheses are disjoint. Hence, $P(B) = P(B \cap A^c) + P(A \cap B) = 0.4 + 0.2 = 0.6$; (b) $P(A \cup B) = P(A) + P(B) - P(A \cap B) = 0.3 + 0.6 - 0.2 = 0.7$; (c) $P(B^c) = 1 - P(B) = 1 - 0.6 = 0.4$; (d) $P(A \cap B^c) = P(A) - P(A \cap B) = 0.1$.

7

Problem 2-14

Mutually exclusive means that $A \cap B = \varnothing$; therefore, $P(A \cap B) = 0$. Statistical independence says that $P(A \cap B) = P(A)P(B)$. Since they are also mutually exclusive, $P(A \cap B) = 0$ which means that either $P(A) = 0$ or $P(B) = 0$ or both.

Problem 2-15

A Venn diagram is provided below. (a) From the areas in the Venn diagram, it follows that $P(A|B)$ = $P(A \cap B)/P(B)$ = $0.125/0.0.5$ = 0.25; (b) $P(B|A)$ = $P(A \cap B)/P(A)$ = $0.125/0.375$ = 0.333; (c) Is $P(A \cap B) = P(A)P(B)$? No, so they are not statistically independent.

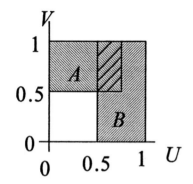

Problem 2-16

(a) $P(A|X)$ = $P(A \cap X)/P(X)$ = $(113/1372)/(372/1372)$ = $113/372$; (b) $P(X|A) = P(A \cap X)/P(A) = 113/662$; (c) $P(B|X)$ = $P(B \cap X)/P(X) = 57/372$; (d) $P(X|B) = 57/348$; (e) $P(C|X)$ = $202/372$; (f) $P(X|C) = 202/362$; (g) $P(A|Y) = 207/406$; (h) $P(Y|A) = 207/662$; (i) $P(B|Y) = 116/406$; (j) $P(Y|B) = 116/348$; (k) $P(C|Y) = 83/406$; (l) $P(Y|C) = 83/362$; (m) $P(A|Z) = 342/594$; (n) $P(Z|A) = 342/662$; (o) $P(B|Z) = 175/594$; (p) $P(Z|B) = 175/348$; (q) $P(C|Z) = 77/594$; (r) $P(Z|C) = 77/362$.

Problem 2-17

$E_5 = \{$only 1 tail$\}$; $E_6 = \{$exactly 2 tails$\}$; (a) $P(E_5) = P(t_1h_2$ or $h_2t_1) = 2/4 = 1/2 = P$(exactly one tail); (b) $P(E_6) = P(t_1t_2) = 1/4 = P$(two tails); (c) $P\{E_5 \cap E_6\} = P$ (impossible event) $= 0$; (d) $P\{E_5 \cup E_6\} = P(t_1h_2$ or h_1t_2 or $t_1t_2) = 3/4 = P$(one or more tails).

Problem 2-18

$A = \{$sum of spots up $= 7\} = \{(1, 6); (2, 5); (3, 4); (4, 3); (5, 2); (6, 1)\}$; $B = \{$sum of spots up $= 11\}$ $= \{(5, 6); (6, 5)\}$. Therefore, $P(A) = 6/36 = 1/6$ and $P(B) = 2/36 = 1/18$. Events A and B can't happen simultaneously, so $P(A \cap B) = 0$. Since $P(A \cap B) \neq P(A)P(B)$, they are not statistically independent.

Problem 2-19

(a) $P(X|C) = P(C \cap X)/P(C) = (202/1372)/(362/1372) = 202/362$; (b) $P(Y|C) = P(C \cap Y)/P(C) = 83/362$; (c) $P(Z|C) = P(C \cap Z)/P(C) = 77/362$.

Problem 2-20

(a) P(nickel) $= P$(nickel I box 1)P(box 1)$+$ P(nickel I box 1)P(box 1)$+$ P(nickel I box 1)P(box 1)

$= (10/45)(1/3) + (5/40)(1/3) + (5/20)(1/3) = 43/216$;

(b) P(dime) $= P$(dime I box 1)P(box 1)$+$ P(dime I box 1)P(box 1)$+$ P(dime I box 1)P(box 1)

$= (5/45)(1/3) + (20/40)(1/3) + (10/20)(1/3) = 10/27$;

(c) P(quarter)$=P$(quarter I box 1)P(box 1)$+$ P(quarter I box 1)P(box 1) $+$ P(quarter I box 1)P(box 1)

$= (30/45)(1/3) + (15/40)(1/3) + (5/20)(1/3) = 31/72$.

Problem 2-21

(a) $P(S = 0 \mid R = 1) = P(R = 1 \mid S = 0)P(S = 0)/P(R = 1)$

But $P(R = 1) = P(R = 1 \mid S = 0)P(S = 0) + P(R = 1 \mid S = 1)P(S = 1)$

$= (0.01)(1/2) + (0.995)(1/2) = 0.5025$

So $P(S = 0 \mid R = 1) = (0.01)(1/2)/(0.5025) = 2/201 \cong 0.01$

(b) $P(S = 1 \mid R = 1) = P(R = 1 \mid S = 1)P(S = 1)/P(R = 1)$

$= (0.995)(1/2)/(0.5025) = 0.99$

(c) $P(S = 0 \mid R = 0) = P(R = 0 \mid S = 0)P(S = 0)/P(R = 0)$

$= (0.995)(1/2)/(0.5025) = 0.99$

But $P(R = 0) = P(R = 0 \mid S = 0)P(S = 0) + P(R = 0 \mid S = 1)P(S = 1)$

$= (0.99)(1/2) + (0.005)(1/2) = 0.4975$

So $P(S = 0 \mid R = 0) = (0.99)(1/2)/(0.4975) = 2/201 \cong 0.995$

(d) $P(S = 1 \mid R = 0) = P(R = 0 \mid S = 1)P(S = 1)/P(R = 0)$

$= (0.005)(1/2)/(0.4975) \cong 0.005$

Problem 2-22

(a) P(no rain) $= P$(no rain I cloudy)P(cloudy) $+ P$(no rain I not cloudy)P(not cloudy)

$= (0.1)(2/3) + (0.7)(1/3) = 0.3$;

(b) P(cloudy I no rain) $= P$(no rain I cloudy)P(cloudy)$/P$(no rain) $= (0.1)(2/3)/(0.9) = 2/9$;

(c) P(not cloudy I rain) $= P$(rain Inot cloudy)P(not cloudy)$/P$(rain) $= (0.3)(1/3)/(0.7) = 1/7$.

Problem 2-23

(a)

$$P(X = 2 \mid Y = 2) = P(Y = 2 \mid X = 2)P(X = 2)/P(Y = 2)$$

$$\text{but} \quad P(Y = 2) = \sum_{i=0}^{3} P(Y = 2 \mid X = i)P(X = i)$$

$$= (0.02)(0.1) + (0.005)(0.3) + (0.97)(0.3) + (0.02)(0.3) = 0.3005$$

$$\text{so} \quad P(X = 2 \mid Y = 2) = (0.97)(0.3)/(0.3005) = 0.9684$$

Problem 2-23 - continued

(b) $P(X = 0 \mid Y = 2) = (0.02)(0.1)/(0.3005) = 0.0067$; (c) $P(X = 1 \mid Y = 2) = (0.005)(0.3)/(0.3005) = 0.005$; (d) $P(X = 3 \mid Y = 1) = (0.03)(0.3)/(0.308) = 0.0292$.

Problem 2-24

Let D denote "defective" and F denote "fails test". Then

$$P(D \mid F) = \frac{P(F \mid D)P(D)}{P(F)}$$

Use theorem on total probability to get denominator:

$$P(F) = P(F \mid D)P(D) + P(F \mid \overline{D})P(\overline{D})$$

$$= (0.02)(0.01) + (0.01)(1 - 0.01) = 0.0101$$

[handwritten: 0.98 ... 0.0197]

Thus

[handwritten: 0.98]

$$P(D \mid F) = \frac{(0.02)(0.01)}{0.0101} = 0.0198$$

[handwritten: 0.0197 ... 0.4974]

Similarly, we have

$$P(\overline{D} \mid \overline{F}) = \frac{P(\overline{F} \mid \overline{D})P(\overline{D})}{P(\overline{F})}$$

Also

[handwritten: 0.0197   0.9803]

$$P(\overline{F}) = 1 - P(F) = 1 - 0.0101 = 0.9899$$

so

$$P(\overline{D} \mid \overline{F}) = \frac{(0.99)(0.99)}{0.9899} = 0.9901$$

[handwritten: 0.9803 ... 0.9997]

10

Problem 2-25

$$P(\overline{U}) = 0.95, \quad P(U) = 0.05$$

$$P(P \mid U) = 0.98, \quad P(P \mid \overline{U}) = 0.01$$

where U denotes "user" and P denotes "testing postive". By the theorem on total probability

$$P(P) = P(P \mid U)P(U) + P(P \mid \overline{U})P(\overline{U}) = (0.98)(0.05) + (0.01)(0.95) = 0.0585$$

By Bayes' theorem,

$$P(\overline{U} \mid P) = \frac{P(P \mid \overline{U})P(\overline{U})}{P(P)} = \frac{(0.01)(0.95)}{0.0585} = 0.1624$$

This conditional probability is surprisingly high. One would hope that if a person tests positive, then the probability of them being a nonuser would be very, very small; i.e., that the probability of a false indication on a positive test is remote. Let's compute the probability that if a person tests negative that they really are a user:

$$P(U \mid \overline{P}) = \frac{P(\overline{P} \mid U)P(U)}{P(\overline{P})} = \frac{(1 - 0.98)(0.05)}{0.9415} = 0.0011$$

This conditional probability appears to be much more acceptable.

Problem 2-26

Following the solution to Example 2-12, let

$$\text{"selected car"} = \text{sc}$$
$$\text{"goat revealed"} = \text{gr}$$

The prior probabilities are

$$P(\text{sc}) = \frac{1}{n}; \quad P(\text{sg}) = \frac{n - 1}{n}$$

For game show host randomly selecting the curtain:

$$P(\text{gr} \mid \text{sc}) = 1; \quad P(\text{gr} \mid \text{gs}) = \frac{n - 2}{n - 1} \quad \text{(host randomly selects)}$$

For game show host using prior knowledge:

$$P(\text{gr} \mid \text{sc}) = 1; \quad P(\text{gr} \mid \text{gs}) = 1 \quad \text{(host uses prior knowledge)}$$

Using the theorem on total probability

$$P(\text{gr}) = P(\text{gr} \mid \text{sc})P(\text{sc}) + P(\text{gr} \mid \text{gs})P(\text{gs})$$

$$= 1 \times \frac{1}{n} + \frac{n-2}{n-1} \times \frac{n-1}{n} = \frac{n-1}{n} \quad \text{(host randomly selects)}$$

and

$$P(\text{gr}) = P(\text{gr} \mid \text{sc})P(\text{sc}) + P(\text{gr} \mid \text{gs})P(\text{gs})$$

$$= 1 \times \frac{1}{n} + 1 \times \frac{n-1}{n} = 1 \quad \text{(host uses prior knowledge)}$$

Hence, by Bayes' theorem

$$P(\text{sc} \mid \text{gr}) = \frac{P(\text{gr} \mid \text{sc})P(\text{sc})}{P(\text{gr})} = \frac{1 \times (1/n)}{(n-1)/n} = \frac{1}{n-1} \quad \text{(host randomly selects)}$$

and

$$P(\text{sc} \mid \text{gr}) = \frac{P(\text{gr} \mid \text{sc})P(\text{sc})}{P(\text{gr})} = \frac{1 \times (1/n)}{1} = \frac{1}{n} \quad \text{(host uses prior knowledge)}$$

Problem 2-27

The number of possible n-long sequences using the numbers 1 through 365 is 365^n. This represents the number of possible birthdays of n persons in the room. For the probability of two or more persons having the same birthday, we use P(at least 2 out of n persons having same birthday) = 1 - P(none having the same birthday). The number of n-sequences where no two days is the same is given by $365 \times 364 \times \ldots \times (365 - n + 1)$ so, by the principle of equal likelihood, the probability of two or more persons out of n having the same birthday is

$$P(\text{two or more with same birthday}) = 1 - \frac{365 \times 364 \times \cdots (365 - n + 1)}{365^n}$$

$$= 1 - \frac{365!}{(365 - n)! \times 365^n}$$

Some numerical values are given below:

> For 20.0 persons in the room, the probability is 0.41
> For 21.0 persons in the room, the probability is 0.44
> For 22.0 persons in the room, the probability is 0.48
> For 23.0 persons in the room, the probability is 0.51
> For 24.0 persons in the room, the probability is 0.54
> For 25.0 persons in the room, the probability is 0.57
> For 26.0 persons in the room, the probability is 0.6
> For 27.0 persons in the room, the probability is 0.63
> For 28.0 persons in the room, the probability is 0.65
> For 29.0 persons in the room, the probability is 0.68
> For 30.0 persons in the room, the probability is 0.71

Note that for 23 persons, the probability is just over 0.5.

Problem 2-28

The number of possible five card hands drawn from a 52 card deck is $\binom{52}{5}$. Suppose we select

the four aces in the deck. How many ways are there to select the other card? Since there are only 48 cards left to choose from, the answer is 48. Hence, there are 48 hands containing the four aces and the desired probability is

$$P(\text{four aces}) = \frac{48}{\binom{52}{5}} = \frac{(48)(5!)(47!)}{52!} = \frac{(48)(120)}{52 \times 51 \times 50 \times 49 \times 48} = 1.8469 \times 10^{-5}$$

By this same reasoning, the probability of getting three aces is

$$P(\text{four aces}) = \frac{\binom{48}{2}}{\binom{52}{5}} = \frac{(48!)(5!)(47!)}{(46!)(2!)(52!)} = \frac{47}{(5)(17)(26)(49)} = 4.3402 \times 10^{-4}$$

which is considerably better odds.

Problem 2-29

(a) The number of 13-card hands from a 52 card deck is $\binom{52}{13}$. The number of hands with all hearts is one. Thus, the probability of getting a hand with all hearts is

$$P(\text{all hearts}) = \frac{1}{\binom{52}{13}} = \frac{(13!)(39!)}{52!} = 1.5748 \times 10^{-12}$$

(b) The probability is four times the probability of part (a) since there are four possible hands with all the same suit.

Problem 2-30

The probability is

$$P(4 \text{ men and } 3 \text{ women}) = \frac{\binom{10}{3}\binom{12}{4}}{\binom{22}{7}} = 0.3483$$

Problem 2-31

The answer will be given for arbitrary m and n and then specialized. If you guess on all n questions and you must answer at least m correctly, the result is

$$P(\text{answer at least } m \text{ out of } n) = P(m \text{ correct}) + P(m+1 \text{ correct}) + \cdots + P(n \text{ correct})$$

$$= \frac{\binom{n}{m}}{2^n} + \frac{\binom{n}{m+1}}{2^n} + \cdots + \frac{\binom{n}{n}}{2^n}$$

For $m = 8$ and $n = 10$, the result is $(45 + 10 + 1)/2^{10} = 0.0547$, which isn't very encouraging.

If the answer is known to one question, then the answer is the same as guessing on $m - 1$ questions. So if you need to answer 8 out of 10 questions correctly in order to pass, the probability is $(120 + 45 + 10 + 1)/2^{10} = 0.1719$, which still isn't very good odds.

CHAPTER 3
SINGLE RANDOM VARIABLES AND PROBABILITY DISTRIBUTIONS

Problem 3-1

A table of values for the random variable is given below:

die 2→ / die 1↓	1	2	3	4	5	6
1	0	-1	-2	-3	-4	-5
2	1	0	-1	-2	-3	-4
3	2	1	0	-1	-2	-3
4	3	2	1	0	-1	-2
5	4	3	2	1	0	-1
6	5	4	3	2	1	0

All probabilities are 1/36, so

$$P(X = 0) = \frac{1}{6}; \quad P(X = 1) = \frac{5}{36}; \quad P(X = 2) = \frac{4}{36};$$

$$P(X = 3) = \frac{3}{36}; \quad P(X = 4) = \frac{2}{36}; \quad P(X = 5) = \frac{1}{36};$$

$$P(X = -1) = \frac{5}{36}; \quad P(X = -2) = \frac{4}{36}; \quad P(X = -3) = \frac{3}{36};$$

$$P(X = -4) = \frac{2}{36}; \quad P(X = -5) = \frac{1}{36}$$

Problem 3-2

Toss three coins. The possible outcomes are:

0 heads	t_1	t_2	t_3
1 head	t_1	t_2	h_3
1 head	t_1	h_2	t_3

1 head	h_1	t_2	t_3
2 heads	t_1	h_2	h_3
2 heads	h_1	t_2	h_3
2 heads	h_1	h_2	t_3
3 heads	h_1	h_2	h_3

From this we can determine the probabilities of 0, 1, 2, or 3 heads:

no. of heads	no. of ways	probability
0	1	$(1/2)^3$
1	3	$3\,(1/2)^3$
2	3	$3\,(1/2)^3$
3	1	$(1/2)^3$

Problem 3-3

draw 1	draw 2	draw 3	RV $X =$	probability
r	r	r	3	$(10/50)(9/49)(8/48)$
r	r	b	5	$(10/50)(9/49)(20/48)$
r	b	r	5	$(10/50)(20/49)(9/48)$
b	r	r	5	$(20/50)(10/49)(9/48)$
r	b	b	7	$(10/50)(20/49)(19/48)$
b	r	b	7	$(20/50)(10/49)(19/48)$
b	b	r	7	$(20/50)(19/49)(10/48)$
w	r	r	7	$(20/50)(10/49)(9/48)$
r	w	r	7	$(10/50)(20/49)(9/48)$
r	r	w	7	$(10/50)(9/49)(20/48)$
b	b	b	9	$(20/50)(19/49)(18/48)$
r	b	w	9	$(10/50)(20/49)(20/48)$

b	b	w	11	(20/50)(19/49)(20/48)
b	w	b	11	(20/50)(20/49)(19/48)
w	b	b	11	(20/50)(20/49)(19/48)
w	w	r	11	(20/50)(19/49)(10/48)
w	r	w	11	(20/50)(10/49)(19/48)
r	w	w	11	(10/50)(20/49)(19/48)
b	w	w	13	(20/50)(20/49)(19/48)
w	b	w	13	(20/50)(20/49)(19/48)
w	w	b	13	(20/50)(19/49)(20/48)
w	w	w	15	(20/50)(19/49)(18/48)

From this tabulation, the following probability mass function for X, the sum of the numbers on the three drawn balls, can be obtained as shown in the following table:

$X =$	$P(X =)$
3	0.0061
5	0.0459
7	0.1429
9	0.0922
11	0.2908
13	0.1939
15	0.0582

Problem 3-4

(a) Yes, all properties are satisfied. (b) No. $F_2(\infty) \neq 1$, but all other properties are satisfied. (c) Yes, as long as $u(x)$ is defined to be 1 at $x = 0$.

Problem 3-5

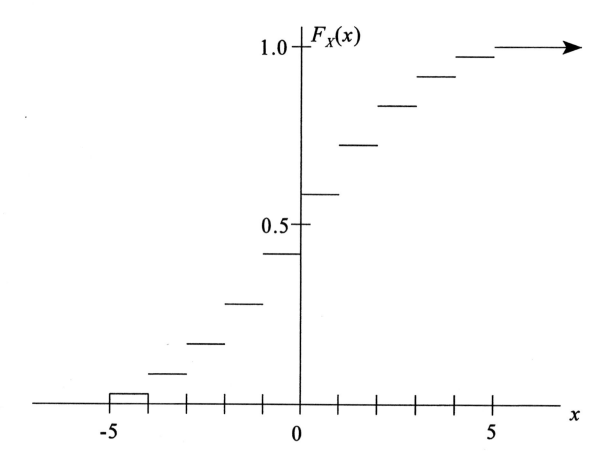

Problem 3-6

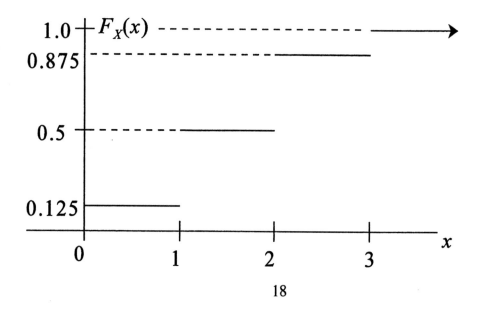

18

Problem 3-7

(a) $P(5 \leq X \leq 7) = F_X(7) - F_X(5) = e^{-1} - e^{-1.4} = 0.1213$; (b) $P(X \leq 3) = F_X(3) = 1 - e^{-0.6} = 0.4512$;

(c) $P(X > 3) = 1 - P(X \leq 3) = 0.5488$.

$P(X < 3) = 0.4512$

$P(X > 3) = 1 - P(X < 3) = 0.5488$

Problem 3-8

$$f_X(x) = \frac{dF_X(x)}{dx} = -(-1/5)e^{-x/5}u(x) = \frac{1}{5}e^{-x/5}u(x)$$

Problem 3-9

(a) The desired probability can be expressed as

$$P(2 \leq X \leq 4) = \int_2^4 \frac{e^{-(x-2)^2/4}}{\sqrt{4\pi}}dx = \int_0^{\sqrt{2}} \frac{e^{-v^2/2}}{\sqrt{2\pi}}dv = \frac{1}{2} - Q(\sqrt{2}), \quad v = \frac{x-2}{\sqrt{2}}$$

Numerical evaluation gives $P(2 \leq X \leq 4) = 0.4214$.

(b) The desired probability is

$$P(X > 4) = \int_4^\infty \frac{e^{-(x-2)^2/4}}{\sqrt{4\pi}}dx = \int_{\sqrt{2}}^\infty \frac{e^{-v^2/2}}{\sqrt{2\pi}}dv = Q(\sqrt{2}) = 0.0786$$

(c) The desired probability is

$$P(X < 2) = \int_{-\infty}^2 \frac{e^{-(x-2)^2/4}}{\sqrt{4\pi}}dx = \int_{-\infty}^0 \frac{e^{-v^2/2}}{\sqrt{2\pi}}dv = Q(\sqrt{2}) = 0.5$$

(d) Let the probabilities for the three parts be P_a, P_b, and P_c, respectively. Then $P_a = 1 - P_b - P_c$.

19

Problem 3-10

(a) A plot and table of values is given below for $n = 6$ and $p = 0.5$:

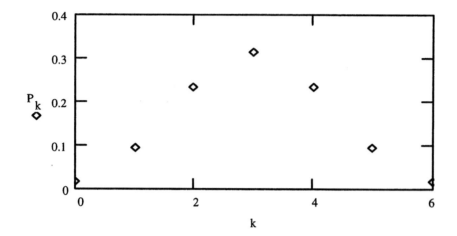

k	P_k
0	0.016
1	0.094
2	0.234
3	0.313
4	0.234
5	0.094
6	0.016

(b) $n = 6$ and $p = 0.1$:

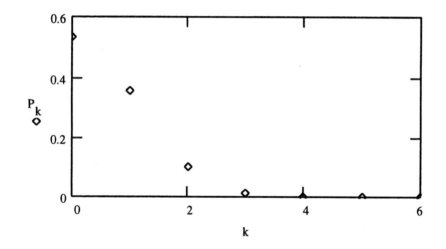

k	P_k
0	0.531
1	0.354
2	0.098
3	0.015
4	0.001
5	$5.4 \cdot 10^{-5}$
6	$1 \cdot 10^{-6}$

(c) $n = 7$ and $p = 0.5$:

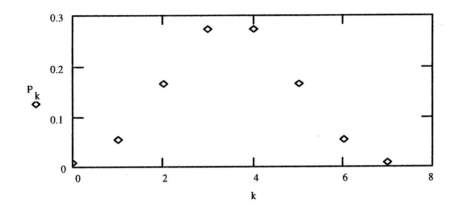

k	P_k
0	0.008
1	0.055
2	0.164
3	0.273
4	0.273
5	0.164
6	0.055
7	0.008

(d) $n = 7$ and $p = 0.1$:

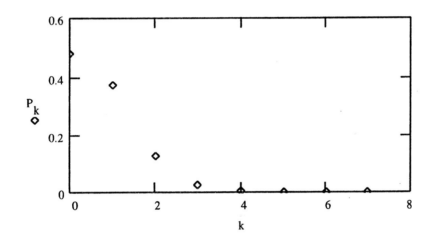

k	P_k
0	0.478
1	0.372
2	0.124
3	0.023
4	0.003
5	$1.701 \cdot 10^{-4}$
6	$6.3 \cdot 10^{-6}$
7	$1 \cdot 10^{-7}$

The maximum is at $\lfloor np \rfloor$ where $\lfloor \ \rfloor$ denotes the "largest integer smaller than" for n even. For n odd, the maximum is bracked by $\lfloor np \rfloor$ and $\lfloor np \rfloor + 1$.

Problem 3-11

(a) The result for exactly k errors is given by a binomial distribution. Thus

$$P(> 3 \text{ errors}) = 1 - \sum_{k=0}^{3} \binom{1000}{k} p^k (1-p)^{n-k}$$

where $p = 10^{-3}$. When expanded, we get

$$P(> 3 \text{ errors}) = 1 - \left[\binom{1000}{0}(0.999)^{1000} + \binom{1000}{1}(10^{-3})(0.999)^{999} + \binom{1000}{2}(10^{-3})^2(0.999)^{998} \right]$$

$$= 1 - [0.3677 + 0.3681 + 0.1840] = 0.08018$$

(b) We now approximate the probability of exactly k errors by the Poisson distribution:

$$P(> 3 \text{ errors}) = 1 - \sum_{k=0}^{3} \frac{(1000)(10^{-3})}{k!} e^{(1000)(10^{-3})} = 1 - [1 + 1 + 0.5]e^{-1} = 0.0803$$

Problem 3-12

The probability of three girls in a four-child family is

$$P(3 \text{ girls}) = \binom{4}{3}\left(\frac{1}{2}\right)^3\left(\frac{1}{2}\right)^1 = 0.25$$

Problem 3-13

(a) The integral of the pdf over all x must be one:

$$\int_0^\infty \frac{A}{(a+x)^2} dx = -A(a+x)^{-1}\Big|_0^\infty = \frac{A}{a} = 1$$

Therefore, $A = a$ [note that the integral starts at 0 because of the $u(x)$].
(b) The integral of the pdf over all x is

$$\int_{-a}^{a} A(a - |x|) dx = 2A \int_0^a (a-x) dx = Aa^2 = 1 \text{ or } A = 1/a^2$$

22

Problem 3-14

Following Example 3-10, we calculate

$$P(W > 10^{-2} \text{ seconds}) = 1 - P(W \le 10^{-2} \text{ seconds}) = 1 - (1 - e^{-(50)(10^{-2})}) = 0.60653$$

where $\lambda = 50$ per second. For 5 milliseconds,

$$P(W > 5 \times 10^{-3} \text{ seconds}) = 1 - P(W \le 5 \times 10^{-3} \text{ seconds}) = 1 - (1 - e^{-0.25}) = 0.7788$$

Problem 3-15

Following Example 3-10 with $\lambda = 100/60 = 1.667$ events per minute,

$$P(W > 1 \text{ minute}) = 1 - P(W \le 1 \text{ minute}) = 1 - (1 - e^{-(5/3)(1)}) = 0.1889$$

For 30 seconds or ½ minute,

$$P(W > 0.5 \text{ minute}) = 1 - P(W \le 0.5 \text{ minute}) = 1 - (1 - e^{-(5/3)(0.5)}) = 0.4346$$

Problem 3-16

Apply the geometric distribution with $p = 0.1$:

$$P(\text{success at try } 5) = p(1 - p)^{k - 1} = 0.1(0.9)^4 = 0.0656$$

For any trial up to and including trial 5, we sum the probabilities for success at trial 1, 2, 3, 4, and 5:

$$P(\text{at trial } 1) = p = 0.1; \quad P(\text{at trial } 2) = p(1 - p) = 0.1(0.9) = 0.09;$$

$$P(\text{at trial } 3) = p(1 - p)^3 = 0.1(0.9)^2 = 0.081;$$

$$P(\text{at trial } 4) = p(1 - p)^3 = 0.1(0.9)^3 = 0.0729$$

We already have the result for trial 5. Summing these, we obtain

$$P(\text{success at any trial up to and including } 5)$$

$$= 0.1 + 0.09 + 0.081 + 0.0729 + 0.0656 = 0.4095$$

At trial 10, $P(\text{success at trial } 10) = 0.1(0.9)^9 = 0.0387$.

Problem 3-17

(a) Apply the Pascal distribution $n = 25$, $k = 3$, and $p = 0.01$:

$$P(X = 3) = \binom{25 - 1}{3 - 1}(0.01)^3(1 - 0.01)^{25 - 3} = 0.00022$$

(b) Again use the Pascal distribution with $n = 100$, $k = 3$, and $p = 0.01$:

$$P(X = 3) = \binom{100 - 1}{3 - 1}(0.01)^3(1 - 0.01)^{100 - 3} = 0.00183$$

(c) Now $n = 500$:

$$P(X = 3) = \binom{500 - 1}{3 - 1}(0.01)^3(1 - 0.01)^{500 - 3} = 0.0008414$$

Note that the probability in (c) has decreased from that in (b) indicating that the third error has long since occurred.

Problem 3-18

Apply the hypergeometric distribution: 0.1% defective says that $p = 0.001$. Also, we can assume that in the population $(0.001) \times (10000) = 10$ are defective. Take $N = 10000$ and $n = 5$:

$$P(\geq 1 \text{ defective}) = 1 - P(0 \text{ defective}) = 1 - \frac{\binom{10}{0}\binom{10000 - 10}{5 - 0}}{\binom{10000}{5}} = 1 - 0.9950 = 0.005$$

Note that considerable canceling can be done in the factorials of the binomial coefficients.

Problem 3-19

Following Example 3-13, let $a = -3$ and $b = 5$; thus $Y = aX + b$ or $X = (Y - b)/a = -0.333(Y - 5)$ and

$$f_Y(y) = |a|^{-1}f_X[(y - b)/a] = 0.333f_X[0.333(y - 5)] = \begin{cases} 0.111, & -7 \leq y \leq 2 \\ 0, & \text{otherwise} \end{cases}$$

24

Problem 3-20

(a) There are two solutions to $y = x^2$:

$$x_1 = \sqrt{y} \text{ and } x_2 = -\sqrt{y}$$

with derivatives

$$\frac{dx_1}{dy} = \frac{1}{2\sqrt{y}} \text{ and } \frac{dx_2}{dy} = -\frac{1}{2\sqrt{y}}$$

Thus

$$f_Y(y) = \sum_{i=1}^{2} f_X(x) \left| \frac{dx_i}{dy} \right|_{x_i = g^{-1}(y)} = \frac{1.5e^{-2\sqrt{y}}}{2\sqrt{y}} + \frac{1.5e^{-2\sqrt{y}}}{2\sqrt{y}} = \frac{1.5e^{-2\sqrt{y}}}{\sqrt{y}}, \ y \geq 0$$

The pdf is 0 for $y < 0$.

(b) Again we have two solutions to $y = |x|$, which are

$$x_1 = y \ (x > 0) \text{ and } x_2 = -y \ (x < 0)$$

with derivatives

$$\frac{dx_1}{dy} = 1 \text{ and } \frac{dx_2}{dy} = -1$$

The pdf of Y is

$$f_Y(y) = \sum_{i=1}^{2} f_X(x) \left| \frac{dx_i}{dy} \right|_{x_i = g^{-1}(y)} = 1.5e^{-3y}(1)(2) = 3e^{-3y}, \ y > 0$$

The pdf is 0 for $y < 0$.

(c) We have only one solution: $x = y$ and $dx/dy = 1$, $y > 0$. Y has a finite probability of being zero, which is equal to the probability that $X < 0$. This is 1/2. Thus,

$$f_Y(y) = 0.5\delta(y) + 1.5e^{-3y}u(y)$$

Problem 3-21

The given transformation and its inverse are

$$y = \cos(\theta), \quad \theta = \cos^{-1}(y)$$

The derivative of the inverse transformation can be obtained by differentiating the second equation, or alternatively as follows:

$$\frac{dy}{d\theta} = -\sin(\theta) \quad \text{or} \quad \frac{d\theta}{dy} = -\frac{1}{\sin(\theta)}$$

But $\sin^2\theta = 1 - \cos^2\theta = 1 - y^2$, so the latter equation can be written in terms of y as

$$\frac{d\theta}{dy} = -\frac{1}{\sqrt{1 - y^2}}$$

Since Θ is uniformly distributed in the interval $[-\pi, \pi]$ we only have to consider solutions of the inverse transformation in this range. A sketch of $\cos\theta$ shows that there are two, and since $\cos\theta$ is even, we can double the result for one to get the pdf of Y:

$$f_Y(y) = \sum_{i=1}^{2} f_\Theta(\theta) \left| \frac{d\theta}{dy} \right|_{\theta_i = g^{-1}(y)} = \frac{1}{2\pi} \times \frac{1}{\sqrt{1 - y^2}} \times 2, \quad |y| \le 1$$

The $1/(2\pi)$ is due $f_X(x)$ and the 2 is due to the two solutions of the inverse transformation. Outside the interval $[-\pi, \pi]$ the pdf of Y is zero. Thus

$$f_Y(y) = \begin{cases} \dfrac{1}{\pi\sqrt{1 - y^2}}, & |y| \le 1 \\[2ex] 0, & \text{otherwise} \end{cases}$$

Problem 3-22

The transformation and its inverse are $y = -\ln x$ and $x = e^{-y}$ with $\dfrac{dx}{dy} = -e^{-y}$. Thus

$$f_Y(y) = 1 \times e^{-y}, 0 \le y \le \infty \text{ and } 0 \text{ otherwise}$$

Problem 3-23

By definition, the expectation of X is

$$E(X) = \sum_{k=0}^{\infty} k \frac{a^k}{k!} e^{-a} = \sum_{k=1}^{\infty} \frac{a^k}{(k-1)!} e^{-a}$$

$$= a \sum_{k=1}^{\infty} \frac{a^{k-1}}{(k-1)!} e^{-a} = a e^{-a} \sum_{j=0}^{\infty} \frac{a^j}{j!} \quad (j = k - 1)$$

$$= a e^{-a} e^a = a$$

To obtain the variance, we need the second moment, which is

$$E(X) = \sum_{k=0}^{\infty} k^2 \frac{a^k}{k!} e^{-a} = a e^{-a} \sum_{k=1}^{\infty} \frac{k a^{k-1}}{(k-1)!} e^{-a} = a e^{-a} \sum_{j=0}^{\infty} (j+1) \frac{a^j}{j!} \quad (j = k - 1)$$

$$= a e^{-a} \left[\sum_{j=1}^{\infty} \frac{a^j}{(j-1)!} + \sum_{j=0}^{\infty} \frac{a^j}{j!} \right] = a e^{-a} [a e^a + e^a] = a^2 + a$$

The variance is

$$\text{var}(X) = E(X^2) - E^2(X) = a^2 + a - a^2 = a$$

Problem 3-24

(a) The nth moment is given by

$$E(X^n) = \int_{-\infty}^{\infty} x^n [0.1\delta(x-1) + 0.3\delta(x-3) + 0.5\delta(x-4) + 0.1\delta(x-7)] dx$$

$$= 0.1(1)^n + 0.3(3)^n + 0.5(4)^n + 0.1(7)^n$$

27

(b) Evaluating the above for $n = 1$ and $n = 2$, we obtain $E(X) = 3.7$ and $E(X^2) = 15.7$ so that $\text{var}(X) = 15.7 - (3.7)^2 = 2.01$.

(c) The expression for the nth central moment is obtained by subtracting $E(X) = 3.7$ from X above and then take $E[(X - 3.7)^n]$. A general expression may be obtained by applying the binomial theorem of algebra. The derivation is

$$E[(X - 3.7)^n] = \int_{-\infty}^{\infty} (x - 3.7)^n [0.1\delta(x - 1) + 0.3\delta(x - 3) + 0.5\delta(x - 4) + 0.1\delta(x - 7)]\,dx$$

$$= \sum_{i=0}^{n} \binom{n}{i} 3.7^{n-i}[0.1 + 0.3\times3^i + 0.5\times4^i + 0.1\times7^i]$$

Problem 3-25

A sketch is provided to the right for computational purposes. From the sketch, it is apparent tht the mode is

$$\int_{0}^{m} 2x\,dx = \int_{m}^{1} 2x\,dx$$

at $x = 1$. The median, m, is defined by Integration yields $m = 2^{-1/2}$. The mean, μ, is given by

$$\mu = \int_{0}^{1} x(2x)\,dx = 2\frac{x^3}{3}\bigg|_{0}^{1} = \frac{2}{3}$$

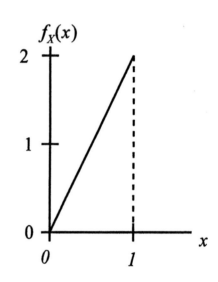

Problem 3-26

Let X = number of spots on the up face. Then the pdf is

$$f_X(x) = \frac{1}{6}[\delta(x - 1) + \delta(x - 2) + \delta(x - 3) + \delta(x - 4) + \delta(x - 5) + \delta(x - 6)]$$

The nth moment of X is

$$E(X^n) = \int_{-\infty}^{\infty} x^n f_X(x) \, dx$$

$$= \int_{-\infty}^{\infty} \frac{x^n}{6} [\delta(x-1) + \delta(x-2) + \delta(x-3) + \delta(x-4) + \delta(x-5) + \delta(x-6)] \, dx$$

$$= \frac{1}{6}[1 + 2^n + 3^n + 4^n + 5^n + 6^n]$$

This can be evaluated for $n = 1$ and $n = 2$ to give the following values for the mean and second moment: $E(X) = 21/6$ and $E(X^2) = 91/6$.

Problem 3-27

Solution 1: Use conditional expectation. Let H = hypothesis that a 7 is obtained on first roll. Let X = number of rolls until first 7. On any roll

$$P(H) = P(3 \& 4 \text{ or } 4 \& 3 \text{ or } 2 \& 5 \text{ or } 5 \& 2 \text{ or } 1 \& 6 \text{ or } 6 \& 1) = \frac{5}{6}$$

The expectation of X can be found using conditional expectation as

$$E(X) = E_H[E_{X|H}(X \mid H)]$$

where the subscript indicates the random variable which expectation is taken with respect to (the first is the expectation of X given H). Thus

$$E(X) = P(H)E(X \mid H) + [1 - P(H)]E(X \mid \overline{H}) = \frac{1}{6} \times 1 + \left(1 - \frac{1}{6}\right)[1 + E(X)]$$

(Note that if H occurs we only need one roll.) Solve for $E(X)$ to get

$$E(X) = 6$$

Solution 2: Let p = probability of a 7 on any roll. Then

$$E(X) = 1 \times p + 2(1-p)p + 3(1-p)^2 p + \cdots = p(1 + 2q + 3q^2 + 4q^3 + \cdots)$$

where $q = 1 - p$. Use the formula for sum of a geometric series, which is

$$1 + q + q^2 + \cdots = \frac{1}{1-q}, \quad |q| < 1$$

(Long division can be used to demonstrate this.) Use differentiation to show that

$$\frac{d}{dq}\left[\frac{1}{1-q}\right] = 0 + 1 + 2q + 3q^2 + \;\; = -(1-q)^{-2}(-1) = \frac{1}{(1-q)^2}$$

Thus

$$E(X) = \frac{p}{(1-q)^2} = \frac{p}{p^2} = \frac{1}{p} = 6$$

Problem 3-28

$Y = aX + b$ with $\mu_X = 2$ and $\sigma_X = 3$. Thus

$$E(Y) = aE(X) + b = 2a + b = 0 \quad \text{and} \quad \text{var}(Y) = a^2\text{var}(X) = 9a^2 = 1$$

Solve for a and b to get $a = \pm\, 1/3$ and $b = \mp\, 2/3$. Therefore

$$Y = \frac{1}{3}X - \frac{2}{3} \quad \text{or} \quad Y = -\frac{1}{3}X + \frac{2}{3}$$

Problem 3-29

(a) The mean is

$$E(Y) = E(X^3) = \int_2^5 x^3 \frac{dx}{3} = \frac{x^4}{12}\bigg|_2^5 = \frac{5^4 - 2^4}{12} = 50.75$$

The mean-square value is

$$E(Y^2) = E(X^6) = \int_2^5 x^6 \frac{dx}{3} = \frac{x^7}{12}\bigg|_2^5 = \frac{5^7 - 2^7}{12} = 3714.143$$

Thus the variance is

$$\sigma_Y^2 = 3714.143 - (50.75)^2 = 1138.58$$

(b) For an exponential pdf with parameter $\alpha = 3$, we have

$$E(Y) = E(X^3) = \int_2^5 x^3 \left(3 e^{-3x}\right) dx = \frac{1}{27} \int_0^\infty u^3 e^{-u} du = \frac{\Gamma(4)}{27} = \frac{3!}{27} = \frac{2}{9}$$

The mean-square value and variance are

$$E(Y^2) = E(X^6) = \int_2^5 x^6 \left(3 e^{-3x}\right) dx = \frac{1}{3^6} \int_0^\infty u^6 e^{-u} du = \frac{\Gamma(7)}{3^6} = \frac{6!}{3^6} = \frac{80}{81}$$

$$\sigma_Y^2 = 80/81 - (2/9)^2 = 0.9383$$

Problem 3-30

The characteristic function is

$$M_X(jv) = E\left(e^{jvX}\right)$$

$$= \int_{-\infty}^{\infty} [0.1\delta(x-1) + 0.3\delta(x-3) + 0.5\delta(x-4) + 0.1\delta(x-7)]e^{jvx}\,dx$$

$$= 0.1e^{jv} + 0.3e^{j3v} + 0.5e^{j4v} + 0.1e^{j7v}$$

The mean can be found as

$$E(X) = \left.\frac{dM_X(jv)}{d(jv)}\right|_{jv=0}$$

$$= 0.1e^{jv} + 0.3(3)e^{j3v} + 0.5(4)e^{j4v} + 0.1(7)e^{j7v}\Big|_{jv=0} = 3.7$$

The second moment is given by

$$E(X^2) = \left.\frac{d^2M_X(jv)}{d(jv)^2}\right|_{jv=0}$$

$$= 0.1e^{jv} + 0.3(3)^2e^{j3v} + 0.5(4)^2e^{j4v} + 0.1(7)^2e^{j7v}\Big|_{jv=0} = 35.3$$
$$15.7$$

The variance is

$$\sigma_Y^2 = 35.3 - (3.7)^2 = 21.61$$
$$15.7 \qquad\qquad 2.01$$

32

Problem 3-31

The characteristic function is

$$M_X(jv) = E(e^{jvX}) = \int_{-\infty}^{\infty} 3e^{-3x}u(x)e^{jvx}dx$$

$$= \int_0^{\infty} 3e^{(jv-3)x}dx$$

$$= \frac{3}{3-jv}$$

The mean is found by differentiating the cdf, which gives

$$m_X = (-j)\frac{dM_X(jv)}{dv}\bigg|_{v=0} = \frac{1}{3}$$

The variance is found by finding the second moment and subtracting the mean squared. The second moment is

$$m_2 = (-j)^2\frac{d^2M_X(jv)}{dv^2}\bigg|_{v=0} = \frac{2}{9}$$

so that the variance is 2/9 - 1/9 = 1/9.

Problem 3-32

In the definition of the characteristic function

$$M_X(jv) = E[e^{jvX}]$$

use the series expansion

$$e^u = 1 + u + \frac{u^2}{2!} + \frac{u^3}{3!} + \cdots = \sum_{k=0}^{\infty} \frac{u^k}{k!}$$

Thus

$$M_X(jv) = E\left[\sum_{k=0}^{\infty} \frac{(jvX)^k}{k!}\right] = \sum_{k=0}^{\infty} \frac{(jv)^k}{k!} E(X^k) \quad \text{QED}$$

Problem 3-33

(a) The pdf of a Poisson random variable is

$$f_X(x) = \sum_{k=0}^{\infty} P(X=k)\delta(x-k) = \sum_{k=0}^{\infty} \frac{a^k}{k!} e^{-a}\delta(x-k)$$

By definition, the characteristic function is

$$M_X(jv) = \int_{-\infty}^{\infty} \left[\sum_{k=0}^{\infty} \frac{a^k}{k!} e^{-a}\delta(x-k)\right] e^{jvx} dx$$

$$= \sum_{k=0}^{\infty} \frac{a^k}{k!} e^{-a} e^{jvk} = e^{-a} \sum_{k=0}^{\infty} \frac{(ae^{jv})^k}{k!}$$

$$= e^{-a} e^{ae^{jv}} = e^{a(e^{jv} - 1)}$$

(b) Use the expansion for e^u used in Problem 3-33 to expand

$$e^{jv} - 1 = \sum_{k=0}^{\infty} \frac{(jv)^k}{k!} - 1 = \sum_{k=1}^{\infty} \frac{(jv)^k}{k!}$$

This allows the characteristic function of part (a) to be written as

$$M_X(jv) = e^{a\sum\limits_{k=1}^{\infty}\frac{(jv)^k}{k!}} = 1 + a\sum_{k=1}^{\infty}\frac{(jv)^k}{k!} + \frac{1}{2!}\left[a\sum_{k=1}^{\infty}\frac{(jv)^k}{k!}\right]^2 + \cdots$$

where the expansion for e^u has been used again. We can regroup terms to write this as

$$M_X(jv) = 1 + a(jv) + (a + a^2)\frac{(jv)^2}{2!} + \left(a + \frac{3!}{2!}a^2\right)\frac{(jv)^3}{3!} + \cdots$$

(c) Comparing this with the expansion for the characteristic function found in Problem 3-33, we see that

$$E(X) = a \quad \text{and} \quad E(X^2) = a + a^2$$

Problem 3-34

(a) Use (3-104) with $k = 2$:

$$P(|X - \mu_X| \geq 2\sigma_X) = \frac{1}{2^2} = 0.25$$

(b) For a random varianbe uniformly distributed in $(-a, a)$, we have

$$\mu_X = 0 \quad \text{and} \quad \sigma_X^2 = \frac{a^2}{3} \quad \text{or} \quad \sigma_X = \frac{a}{\sqrt{3}}$$

Thus

$$P(|X - \mu_X| \geq 2\sigma_X) = P(|X - 0| \geq 2a/\sqrt{3}) = 1 \quad \text{because } 2/\sqrt{3} > 1$$

(c) For the pdf

$$f_X(x) = ae^{-ax}u(x)$$

the mean is $1/a$ and the standard deviation is $1/a$. Thus

$$P(|X - \mu_x| \geq 2\sigma_x) = P(|X - 1/a| \geq 2/a)$$

$$= P(X \geq 1/a) = \int_{1/a}^{\infty} a e^{-ax} dx$$

$$= \int_{1}^{\infty} e^{-u} du = -e^{-u} \Big|_{1}^{\infty} = e^{-1}$$

Problem 3-35

(a) $P(|X - \mu_x| \geq 3\sigma_x) = 1/9 = 0.111$; (b) The probability is 1 because the bound included the whole nonzero region of the pdf of the uniform random variable; (c) Following the derivation in Prob. 3-35(c), it is found that the probability is e^{-2}.

Problem 3-36

The Rayleigh pdf and cdf are given by

$$f_V(v) = \frac{v}{\sigma^2} e^{-v^2/2\sigma^2}, \ v \geq 0, \ \text{and} \ F_V(v) = (1 - e^{-v^2/2\sigma^2}), \ v \geq 0$$

Recall that $U = F_V(V) = g(V)$ is uniform for V distributed according to its probability law (i.e., Rayleigh). Solve this for V to get

$$V = \sqrt{-2\sigma^2 \ln(1 - U)}$$

So, if U is uniform in $(0, 1]$, V will be Rayleigh.

Problem 3-37

See Problem 3-39. Solve

$$U = F_X(X) = \frac{1}{2} + \frac{1}{\pi}\tan^{-1}(X/\alpha)$$

which is (3-41). The result is

$$X = \alpha\tan[\pi(U - 1/2)]$$

so if U is uniformly distributed in (0, 1], X will be Cauchy.

CHAPTER 4
PROBABILITY DISTRIBUTIONS FOR MORE THAN ONE RANDOM VARIABLE

Problem 4-1

(a) Require that $F(\infty, \infty) = 1$. Thus consider

$$\lim_{x, y \to \infty} \left[\frac{Axy}{(2x + 1)(y + 1)} u(x) u(y) \right] = \frac{A}{2} = 1$$

which gives $A = 2$.

(b) Clearly, with the above choice of A, $F(\infty, \infty) = 1$ and $F(-\infty, -\infty) = 0$ because of the unit step functions.

(c) Let x and y be ∞ in turn to get

$$F_X(x) = \frac{2x}{2x + 1} u(x) \text{ and } F_Y(y) = \frac{y}{y + 1} u(y)$$

(d) From (4-7)

$$P(-2 \le X \le 2, 1 \le Y \le 5) = F_{XY}(2, 5) - F_{XY}(-2, 1) - F_{XY}(2, 1) + F_{XY}(-2, 1)$$

$$= \frac{2}{2 \times 2 + 1} \times \frac{5}{5 + 1} - 0 - \frac{2}{2 \times 2 + 1} \times \frac{5}{1 + 1} + 0$$

$$= \frac{2}{15}$$

Problem 4-2

A MATLAB program is given below for obtaining the plot:

```
x =-1:.1:4;
y=-1:.1:4;
Nx=length(x);
Ny=length(y);
F=zeros(Nx,Ny);
for i = 1:Nx
        for j = 1:Ny
                if x(i) <= 0 | y(j) <= 0
                    F(i,j) = 0;
```

```
            else
                F(i,j) = (1-exp(-3*x(i)))*(1-exp(-2*y(j)));

            end
        end
end
clg
mesh(x,y,F), xlabel('x'), ylabel('y'), zlabel('F(x, y)'),...
view(-120,20)
print c:\probab\new\prob4_2 -dps
T=view
```

The plot is shown below:

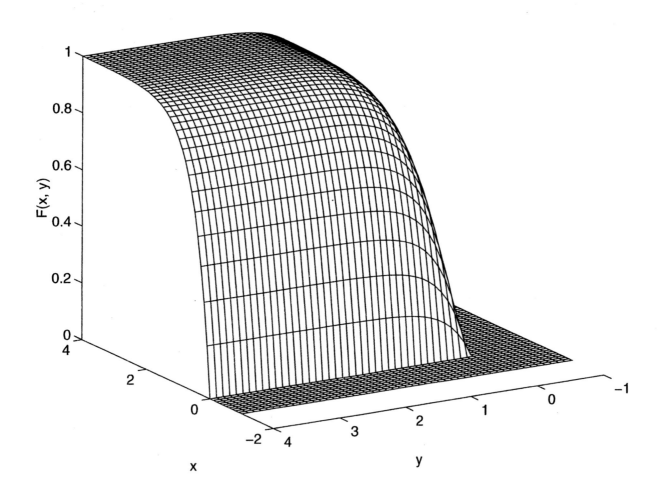

Problem 4-3

(a) The pdf can be found by differentiating the joint cdf partially, once with respect to x and once with respect to y:

$$f(x, y) = \frac{\partial}{\partial x} \frac{\partial}{\partial y} \frac{2x}{2x + 1} \frac{y}{y + 1} u(x) u(y)$$

$$= \frac{\partial}{\partial x} \frac{2x}{2x + 1} \left[\frac{1}{y + 1} - \frac{y}{(y + 1)^2} \right] u(x) u(y)$$

$$= \left[\frac{2}{2x + 1} - \frac{4x}{(2x + 1)^2} \right] \left[\frac{1}{y + 1} - \frac{y}{(y + 1)^2} \right] u(x) u(y)$$

$$= \frac{2}{(2x + 1)^2 (y + 1)^2} u(x) u(y)$$

(b) To get $f_X(x)$ integrate over y:

$$f_X(x) = \int_0^\infty \frac{dy}{(y + 1)^2} \times \frac{2}{(2x + 1)^2} u(y) = \frac{2}{(2x + 1)^2} u(x)$$

Similarly to get $f_Y(y)$ integrate over x:

$$f_Y(y) = \frac{1}{(y + 1)^2} u(y)$$

Problem 4-4

(a) By partial differentiation,

$$f(x, y) = \begin{cases} 6e^{-3x} e^{-2y}, & x \text{ and } y \geq 0 \\ 0, & x \text{ or } y \text{ or both} < 0 \end{cases}$$

A MATLAB program for providing a sketch is given below:

```
x=-1:.1:4;
y=-1:.1:4.;
Nx=length(x);
```

```
Ny=length(y);
F=zeros(Nx,Ny);
for i = 1:Nx
        for j = 1:Ny
                if x(i) <= 0 | y(j) <= 0
                        f(i,j) = 0;
                else
                        f(i,j) = 6*exp(-(3*x(i)+2*y(j)));

                end
        end
end
clg
mesh(x,y,f), x!abel('x'), ylabel('y'), zlabel('f(x, y)'),...
view(-120,20)
print c:\probab\new\prob4_4a -dps
T=view
```

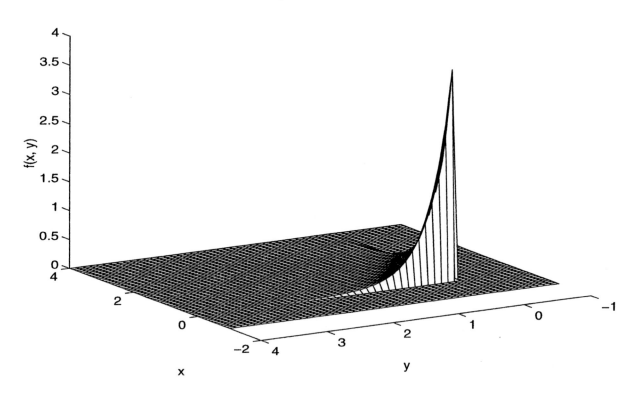

(b) The marginal pdf's are $f_X(x) = 3e^{-3x}u(x)$ and $f_Y(y) = 2e^{-2x}u(y)$.

41

Problem 4-5

(a) The constant A is found from the normalization criterion on the pdf:

$$\int_0^\infty \int_0^\infty Axe^{-x(y+1)}dxdy = 1$$

Carrying out the integrations, we obtain

$$A\int_0^\infty \int_0^\infty xe^{-x(y+1)}dxdy = A\int_0^\infty \left[-\frac{x}{y+1}e^{-x(y+1)}\Big|_0^\infty + \int_0^\infty \frac{e^{-x(y+1)}}{y+1}dx\right]dy$$

$$= A\int_0^\infty \left[0 - \frac{e^{-x(y+1)}}{(y+1)^2}\Big|_0^\infty\right]$$

$$= \int_0^\infty \frac{dy}{(y+1)^2} = -(y+1)^{-1}\Big|_0^\infty = A$$

Thus, $A = 1$.

(b) The marginal pdf's are

$$f_Y(y) = (y+1)^{-2}u(y)$$

and

$$f_X(x) = e^{-x}u(x)$$

42

Problem 4-6

Let T_{ME} = your time of arrival and T_{FR} = friend's time of arrival. Then $60 \le T_{ME} \le 75$ and $50 \le T_{FR} \le 70$. We want the probability $P(T_{ME} > T_{FR})$. The diagram given below will help in the solution.

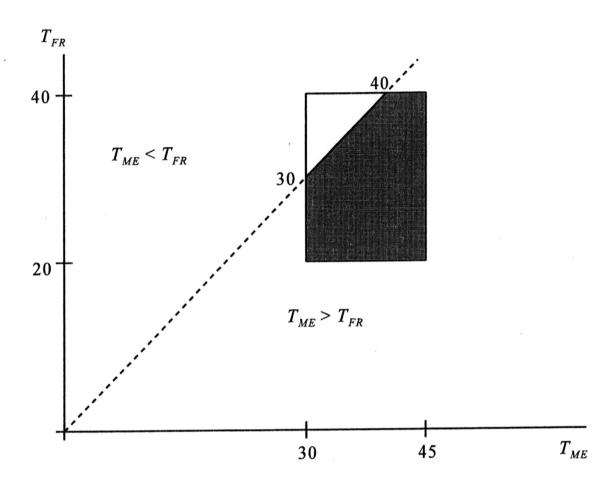

The desired probability is

$$P(T_{ME} > T_{FR}) = \frac{\text{shaded area}}{\text{total area}} = \frac{(15)(20) - 0.5(10)(10)}{(15)(20)} = \frac{5}{6}$$

Problem 4-7

$X\downarrow\ Y\rightarrow$	1	2	3	4	5	6
0	1/12	1/12	1/12	1/12	1/12	1/12
1	1/12	1/12	1/12	1/12	1/12	1/12

43

Problem 4-8

The event $B = \{999 < X \le 1001\}$ and its probability is

$$P(B) = \int_{999}^{1001} e^{-2|x - 1000|} dx = \int_{-1}^{1} e^{-2v} dv = 2\int_{0}^{1} e^{-2v} dv = -e^{-2v}\big|_{0}^{1} = 1 - e^{-2} = 0.865$$

The cdf of X is

$$F_X(x) = \int_{-\infty}^{x} e^{-2|u - 1000|} du = \begin{cases} \displaystyle\int_{-\infty}^{x} e^{-2(1000 - u)} du, & x < 1000 \\[4mm] \dfrac{1}{2} + \displaystyle\int_{1000}^{x} e^{-2(u - 1000)} du, & x \ge 1000 \end{cases}$$

which follows by making use of $|v| = -v$ for $v < 0$ and $|v| = v$ for $v > 0$. Carrying out the integrations, we find that

$$F_X(x) = \begin{cases} 0.5\,e^{2(x - 1000)}, & x < 1000 \\[2mm] 1 - 0.5\,e^{-2(x - 1000)}, & x \ge 1000 \end{cases}$$

Thus

$$P(X \le x \cap B) = \begin{cases} 0, & x < 999 \\[2mm] F_X(x) - F_X(999), & 999 < x \le 1001 \\[2mm] P(B), & x > 1001 \end{cases}$$

and

$$F_{X|B}(x \,|\, B) = \frac{P(X \le x \cap B)}{P(B)}$$

Substituting for $P(X \le x \cap B)$ and differentiating, we obtain

$$f_{X|B}(x|B) = \begin{cases} \dfrac{f_X(x)}{P(B)}, & 999 < x \le 1001 \\ \\ 0, & \text{otherwise} \end{cases}$$

Substituting the appropriate expressions, we find that

$$f_{X|B}(x|B) = \begin{cases} 1.1565\,e^{-2|x-1000|}, & 999 < x \le 1001 \\ \\ 0, & \text{otherwise} \end{cases}$$

Integration of the conditional pdf gives the desired probability:

$$P(999.5 < X \le 1000.5\,|B) = \int_{999.5}^{1000.5} 1.1565\,e^{-2|x-1000|}\,dx$$

$$= \int_{-0.5}^{0.5} 1.1565\,e^{-2|v|}\,dv, \quad v = x - 1000$$

$$= 2\int_{0}^{0.5} 1.1565\,e^{-2|v|}\,dv$$

$$= 1.1565\,(1 - e^{-1}) = 0.7311$$

Problem 4-9

Given S the conditional pdf of X is

$$f_{X|S}(x|s) = \frac{e^{-(x-s)^2/2\sigma^2}}{\sqrt{2\pi\sigma^2}}$$

Given noise alone the conditional pdf of X is

$$f_{X|\bar{S}}(x|\bar{s}) = \frac{e^{-x^2/2\sigma^2}}{\sqrt{2\pi\sigma^2}}$$

The probability of a miss is

$$P_{\text{miss}} = \int_{-\infty}^{A} \frac{e^{-(x-s)^2/2\sigma^2}}{\sqrt{2\pi\sigma^2}} dx = 1 - Q\left(\frac{A-s)}{\sigma}\right)$$

The probability of a false alarm is

$$P_{\text{FA}} = \int_{A}^{\infty} \frac{e^{-(x-s)^2/2\sigma^2}}{\sqrt{2\pi\sigma^2}} dx = Q\left(\frac{A}{\sigma}\right)$$

Assume $A = s/2$. Using a table of Q-functions or a rational approximation for the Q-function we obtain the table of values given below:

s/σ	P_{miss}	P_{FA}
0.5	0.401	0.401
1	0.309	0.309
2	0.159	0.159
4	0.023	0.023
8	3.17×10^{-5}	3.17×10^{-5}

Note that the probabilities of a miss and false alarm are equal. Had we chose some other value for A, this would not have been the case.

Problem 4-10

(a) Yes, they are because we can factor $F(x, y)$ into a function of x alone and a function of y alone.
(b) Yes they are, for the same reason as given in part a.

Problem 4-11

No. We cannot factor $F(x, y)$ into a function of x alone and a function of y alone.

Problem 4-12

(a) The desired expectation is

$$E[\cos(X)\sin(Y)] = \int\limits_{-\infty}^{\infty}\int\limits_{-\infty}^{\infty} \cos(x)\sin(y)e^{-2(|x|+|y|)}\,dx\,dy$$

$$= \int\limits_{-\infty}^{\infty} \cos(x)e^{-2|x|}\,dx \int\limits_{-\infty}^{\infty} \sin(y)e^{-2|y|}\,dy = 0$$

The result is zero because the last integral (over y) has an odd integrand. When integrated over an interval symmetric about 0, the result is zero.

(b) Using the fact that the expectation of a sum is the sum of the expectations of the separate terms in the sum, we obtain

$$E[\cos(X)+\sin(Y)] = \int\limits_{-\infty}^{\infty}\int\limits_{-\infty}^{\infty} \cos(x)e^{-2(|x|+|y|)}\,dx\,dy + \int\limits_{-\infty}^{\infty}\int\limits_{-\infty}^{\infty} \sin(y)e^{-2(|x|+|y|)}\,dx\,dy$$

$$= \int\limits_{-\infty}^{\infty} \cos(x)e^{-2|x|}\,dx\,dy + \int\limits_{-\infty}^{\infty} \sin(y)e^{-2|y|}\,dy = 2\int\limits_{0}^{\infty} \cos(x)e^{-2x}\,dx = 0.8$$

where the oddness of the integrand of the sin-integral has been used to set it equal to zero and a table of integrals has been used to get the integral of the cosine after using the fact that the integrand is even to double it.

Problem 4-13

(a) The general result for the mnth moment is

$$E(X^mY^n) = \int\limits_{-\infty}^{\infty}\int\limits_{-\infty}^{\infty} x^m y^n e^{-2(|x|+|y|)}\,dx\,dy$$

$$= \int\limits_{-\infty}^{\infty} x^m e^{-2|x|}\,dx \int\limits_{-\infty}^{\infty} y^n e^{-2|y|}\,dy = \begin{cases} 0, & m \text{ or } n \text{ or both odd} \\ \dfrac{4m!n!}{2^{m+1}2^{n+1}}, & m \text{ and } n \text{ even} \end{cases}$$

Since the means are zero, the central moments are given by the same expression.

(b) The covariance is

$$C_{XY} = E[(X - \mu_X)(Y - \mu_Y)] = E(XY) = 0$$

(b) $\rho_{XY} = 0$.

Problem 4-14

(a) This is a quarter of a cylinder of radius 1 and height C. Thus, the volume is

$$\text{volume} = \frac{\pi}{4}C = 1 \text{ or } C = \frac{4}{\pi}$$

(b) The desired moments are

$$E(X^mY^n) = \int\int_{\text{area}} x^m y^n \frac{4}{\pi} dx dy$$

Change variables to polar coordinates: $x = r\cos\theta$ and $y = r\sin\theta$; $dxdy = r\,dr\,d\theta$. This results in the integral

$$E(X^mY^n) = \int_0^{\pi/2}\int_0^1 (r\cos\theta)^m (r\sin\theta)^n \frac{4}{\pi} r\,dr\,d\theta$$

$$= \frac{4}{\pi}\int_0^1 r^{m+n+1}dr \int_0^{\pi/2}\cos^m\theta\,\sin^n\theta\,d\theta$$

$$= \frac{4}{\pi}\frac{r^{m+n+2}}{m+n+2}\bigg|_0^1 \int_0^{\pi/2}\cos^m\theta\,\sin^n\theta\,d\theta$$

$$= \frac{4/\pi}{m+n+2}\int_0^{\pi/2}\cos^m\theta\,\sin^n\theta\,d\theta$$

It remains to compute the integral of the cosine-sine powers. It is difficult to get a general result for arbitrary m and n. A few special cases are given in the table below. These can be calculated by using trigonometric identities to simplify the integrands, or a mathematics package such as MATLAB or Mathcad can be used.

Values for

$$\int_0^{\pi/2} \cos^m\theta \sin^n\theta\, d\theta$$

$m\downarrow\ n\rightarrow$	0	1	2	3	4	5
0	1.571	1	0.785	0.667	0.589	0.533
1	1	0.5	0.333	0.25	0.2	0.167
2	0.785	0.333	0.196	0.133	0.098	0.076
3	0.667	0.25	0.133	0.083	0.057	0.042
4	0.589	0.2	0.098	0.057	0.037	0.025
5	0.533	0.167	0.076	0.042	0.025	0.017

These can be used in the experession for the joint moments to compute the values given in the table below:

$m\downarrow\ n\rightarrow$	0	1	2	3	4	5
0	1	0.424	0.25	0.17	0.125	0.097
1	0.424	0.159	0.085	0.053	0.036	0.027
2	0.25	0.085	0.042	0.024	0.016	0.011
3	0.17	0.053	0.024	0.013	0.008	0.005
4	0.125	0.036	0.016	0.008	0.005	0.003
5	0.097	0.027	0.011	0.005	0.003	0.002

(c) The random variables are not uncorrelated because $E(XY) \neq E(X)E(Y)$.

Problem 4-15

The joint pdf is

$$f_{XY}(x, y) = \frac{1}{2}[\delta(x - 1) + \delta(x)]\frac{1}{6}[\delta(y - 1) + \delta(y - 2) + \delta(y - 3) + \delta(y - 4) + \delta(y - 5) + \delta(y - 6)]$$

Note that it can be factored into a pdf for X alone and a pdf of Y alone because the random variables are statistically independent. The joint moments are

$$E(X^m Y^n) = \int_{-\infty}^{\infty} \int_{-\infty}^{\infty} x^m y^n f_{XY}(x, y) \, dx \, dy$$

$$= \frac{1}{2} \int_{-\infty}^{\infty} x^m [\delta(x - 1) + \delta(x)] \, dx \times \frac{1}{6} \int_{-\infty}^{\infty} y^n [\delta(y - 1) + \delta(y - 2) + \delta(y - 3)$$

$$+ \delta(y - 4) + \delta(y - 5) + \delta(y - 6)] \, dy$$

$$= \frac{1}{12} [1^m + 0^m][1^n + 2^n + 3^n + 4^n + 5^n + 6^n]$$

For $m = 1$ and $n = 0$, joint moment = 1/2;
For $m = 0$ and $n = 1$, joint moment = 7/2;
For $m = 1$ and $n = 1$, joint moment = 7/4;
For $m = 2$ and $n = 0$, joint moment = 1/2;
For $m = 0$ and $n = 2$, joint moment = 91/6;
For $m = 2$ and $n = 1$, joint moment = 7/4;
For $m = 1$ and $n = 2$, joint moment = 91/12;
For $m = 2$ and $n = 2$, joint moment = 91/12.

$$\rho_{XY} = [E(XY) - E(X)E(Y)]/\sigma_X \sigma_Y = \frac{21/12 - (1/2)(7/2)}{\sqrt{(1/2 - (1/2)^2)(91/6 - (7/2)^2)}} = 0$$

as we would expect since the random variables are independent.

Problem 4-16

(a) The definition of the characteristic function gives

$$M_X(jv) = E[e^{jvX}] = \int_{-\infty}^{\infty} \frac{e^{-(x - \mu)^2/2\sigma^2}}{\sqrt{2\pi\sigma^2}} e^{jvx} \, dx$$

Let $\lambda = (x - \mu)/\sigma$ to get the form

$$M_X(jv) = \int_{-\infty}^{\infty} \frac{e^{-\lambda^2/2}}{\sqrt{2\pi}} e^{jv(\sigma\lambda + \mu)} \, d\lambda = \frac{e^{jv\mu}}{\sqrt{2\pi}} \int_{-\infty}^{\infty} e^{-0.5(\lambda^2 - j2v\sigma\lambda)} \, d\lambda$$

Complete the square in the exponent in the integrand to get the form

$$M_X(jv) = e^{jv\mu} e^{-0.5\sigma^2 v^2} \int_{-\infty}^{\infty} \frac{e^{-0.5(\lambda^2 - jv\sigma)^2}}{\sqrt{2\pi}} d\lambda$$

$$= e^{jv\mu} e^{-0.5\sigma^2 v^2} \int_{-\infty}^{\infty} \frac{e^{-0.5\psi^2}}{\sqrt{2\pi}} d\psi = e^{jv\mu} e^{-0.5\sigma^2 v^2} = e^{jv\mu - 0.5\sigma^2 v^2}$$

where we note that $\int_{-\infty}^{\infty} \frac{e^{-0.5\psi^2}}{\sqrt{2\pi}} d\psi = 1$ because the integrand is a Gaussian pdf with 0 mean

and unit variance.

(b) Let $Z = X_1 + X_2$ where the sum random variable are independent. Then, the characteristic function of Z is

$$M_Z(jv) = E[e^{jvZ}] = E[e^{jvX_1} e^{jvX_2}] = E[e^{jvX_1}]E[e^{jvX_2}] = M_{X_1}(jv)M_{X_2}(jv)$$

Now use the result for the characteristic function of a Gaussian random variable derived in part a. We get

$$M_Z(jv) = e^{jv\mu_1 - 0.5\sigma_1^2 v^2} e^{jv\mu_2 - 0.5\sigma_2^2 v^2} = e^{jv(\mu_1 + \mu_2) - 0.5(\sigma_1 + \sigma_2)^2 v^2}$$

The result for the sum of two independent Gaussian random variables has the same form as that for a single Gaussian random variable, but with $\mu = \mu_1 + \mu_2$ and $\sigma^2 = \sigma_1^2 + \sigma_2^2$.

(c) Clearly the result of part b generalizes to the sum of any number of independent Gaussian random variables.

Problem 4-17

Let N = number of projectiles fired, and let $H = 1$ if the first projectile hits the target and 0 otherwise. Then, if p = probability of hitting the target on any try,

$$E(N) = E_H\{E[N \mid H]\}$$

$$= pE[N \mid H = 1] + (1 - p)E[N \mid H = 0] = p \times 1 + (1 - p)[1 + E(N)]$$

Solve for $E(N) = 1/p = 1/0.7 = 1.43$ projectiles to hit the target. Round up to 2 projectiles.

Problem 4-18

From the problem statement, the joint pdf of the impact point is the product of two marginal Gaussian pdf's (independence) with the following means and variances:

$$\mu_X = 6 \text{ inches}; \ \mu_Y = -3 \text{ inches}; \ \sigma_X = 2 \text{ inches}; \ \sigma_Y = 4 \text{ inches.}$$

Thus, the pdf of the impact point is

$$f_{XY}(x, y) = \frac{e^{-(x-6)^2/8}}{\sqrt{8\pi}} \ \frac{e^{-(y+3)^2/32}}{\sqrt{32\pi}}$$

Problem 4-19

By definition of a conditional pdf,

$$f_{X|Y}(x|y) = \frac{f_{XY}(x, y)}{f_Y(y)}$$

From (3-28) and (4-52), we obtain

$$f_{X|Y}(x|y) = \sqrt{2\pi\sigma_Y^2} \exp\left[-\frac{1}{2(1-\rho^2)}\left(\frac{(x-\mu_X)^2}{\sigma_X^2} - \frac{2\rho(x-\mu_X)(y-\mu_Y)}{\sigma_X\sigma_Y} + \frac{(y-\mu_Y)^2}{\sigma_Y^2}\right)\right]\left\{2\pi\sigma_X\sigma_Y\sqrt{1-\rho^2}\exp\left[-\frac{(y-\mu_Y)^2}{2\sigma_Y^2}\right]\right\}^{-1}$$

$$= \frac{\exp\left\{-\dfrac{1}{2\sigma_X^2(1-\rho^2)}\left[x^2 - [2\mu_X + 2\rho\sigma_X/\sigma_Y(1-\mu_Y)]x + \mu_X^2 + \dfrac{2\rho\mu_X\sigma_X(y-\mu_X)}{\sigma_Y} + \dfrac{\rho^2\sigma_Y^2(y-\mu_Y)^2}{\sigma_X}\right]\right\}}{\sqrt{2\pi\sigma_X^2(1-\rho^2)}}$$

Complete the square in the exponent of the last equation on x to get the form

$$f_{X|Y}(x|y) = \frac{1}{\sqrt{2\pi\sigma_X^2(1-\rho^2)}} \exp\left\{-\frac{1}{1(1-\rho^2)\sigma_X^2}\left[x - \mu_X - \frac{\rho\sigma_X}{\sigma_Y}(y-\mu_Y)\right]\right\}$$

Clearly, this is the form of a Gaussian pdf with conditional mean and variance given by

$$E(X|Y) = \mu_X + \frac{\rho\sigma_X}{\sigma_Y}(y-\mu_Y) \quad \text{and} \quad \text{var}(X|Y) = \sigma_X^2(1-\rho^2)$$

52

Problem 4-20

By definition of the cdf of Z

$$F_Z(z) = P(Z \leq z) = P(X^2 + Y^2 \leq z) = \int_{X^2+Y^2 \leq z} \frac{e^{-(x^2+y^2)/2\sigma^2}}{2\pi\sigma^2} dxdy$$

Change to polar coordinates: $x = r\cos\theta$, $y = r\sin\theta$, $dx\,dy = r\,dr\,d\theta$

$$F_Z(z) = \int_0^z \int_0^{2\pi} \frac{e^{-r^2/2\sigma^2}}{2\pi\sigma^2} r\,dr\,d\theta = \int_0^{z^2/2\sigma^2} e^{-v}dv = 1 - e^{-z^2/2\sigma^2}, \ z \geq 0$$

Differentiate to get the pdf of Z:

$$f_Z(z) = \frac{z}{\sigma^2} e^{-z^2/2\sigma^2}, \ z \geq 0$$

Problem 4-21

Let $w = x$ and $z = xy$. The inverse transformation is

$$x = w \text{ and } y = z/w$$

The Jacobian is

$$J\begin{pmatrix} x, & y \\ w, & z \end{pmatrix} = \begin{vmatrix} \dfrac{\partial x}{\partial w} & \dfrac{\partial y}{\partial w} \\ \dfrac{\partial x}{\partial z} & \dfrac{\partial y}{\partial z} \end{vmatrix} = \begin{vmatrix} 1 & -\dfrac{z}{w^2} \\ 0 & \dfrac{1}{w} \end{vmatrix} = \frac{1}{w}$$

The joint pdf of W and Z is given by

$$f_{WZ}(w, z) = \frac{f_{XY}(x, y)}{|w|}\Bigg|_{x=w, \ y=z/w} = f_{XY}(w, z/w)$$

To get the marginal pdf of Z, integrate over w:

$$f_Z(z) = \int\limits_{-\infty}^{\infty} f_{XY}(w, z/w)\frac{dw}{|w|} = \int\limits_{-\infty}^{\infty} f_{XY}(z/u, u)\frac{du}{|u|}$$

Problem 4-22

The inverse transformation is

$$x = \frac{1}{\Delta}(du - bv) \text{ and } y = \frac{1}{\Delta}(-cu + av)$$

where $\Delta = ad - bc$ is assumed not to be zero. The Jacobian is

$$J\left(\begin{matrix} x, & y \\ u, & v \end{matrix}\right) = \begin{vmatrix} \dfrac{\partial x}{\partial u} & \dfrac{\partial y}{\partial v} \\[2mm] \dfrac{\partial y}{\partial u} & \dfrac{\partial y}{\partial v} \end{vmatrix} = \frac{1}{\Delta^2}\begin{vmatrix} d & -b \\ -c & a \end{vmatrix} = \frac{1}{\Delta}$$

Use this in (4-52) along with the inverse transformation. The result will be a joint Gaussian pdf.

Problem 4-23

The error in 1 mi = 5280 ft is ±52.8 ft. The pdf of the error in 1 mi is

$$f_E(e) = \begin{cases} \dfrac{1}{105.6}, & -52.8 \le e \le 52.8 \\[3mm] 0, & \text{otherwise} \end{cases}$$

The mean of the error in 1 mi is 0 and the variance is $(105.6)^2/12$. For 10 contiguous measurements the mean and variance are

$$E(D) = 52,800 \text{ ft and } \text{var}(D) = 10\frac{(105.6)^2}{12} = 9292.8 \text{ ft}^2$$

Approximate the measurement for 10 miles as Gaussian by invoking the Central Limit Theorem:

$$P(52{,}800 - 100 \le D \le 52{,}800 + 100) = \int_{52{,}700}^{52{,}900} \frac{e^{-(x - 52{,}800)^2/[2(9292.8)]}}{\sqrt{2\pi(9292.8)}}\,dx = \int_{-100/\sqrt{9292.8}}^{100/\sqrt{9292.8}} \frac{e^{-v^2/2}}{\sqrt{2\pi}}\,dv$$

$$= 1 - 2Q\left(\frac{100}{\sqrt{9292.8}}\right) = 1 - Q(1.03735) = 0.70043$$

Problem 4-24

Follow the sketch of the proof given in the text given on page 130.

Problem 4-25

Let $X = 1$ if a 3 occurs and 0 if a 3 does not occur. Then

$$E(X) = 1{\times}P(3) + 0{\times}P(\text{not } 3) = 1/6$$

The weak law of large numbers becomes

$$P\left[\left|\frac{1}{n}\sum_{i=1}^{n} X_i - \frac{1}{6}\right| \ge \epsilon\right] = 0$$

which says that

$$\frac{1}{n}\sum_{i=1}^{n} X_i \to \frac{1}{6} \text{ as } n \to \infty \text{ in probability}$$

Problem 4-26

(a) From (4-106)

$$\text{var}\left(\sum_{i=1}^{3} X_i\right) = \sum_{i=1}^{3} \text{var}(X_i) + 2\sum \rho_{ij} = 2 + 5 + 3 + 2(0.2 + 0.1 + 0.4) = 11.4$$

(b) From (4-106):

$$\text{var}\left(5X_1 + 2X_2 + X_3\right) = 25(2) + 4(5) + 1(3)$$

$$+ 2[(5)(2)(0.2) + (5)(1)(0.1) + (2)(1)(0.4)] = 79.6$$

CHAPTER 5
ELEMENTARY STATISTICS, EMPIRICAL PROBABILITY DISTRIBUTIONS, AND MORE ON SIMULATION

Problem 5-1

$$E(\bar{x}) = E\left\{\frac{1}{n}\sum_{i=1}^{n} x_i\right\} = \frac{1}{n}E\left\{\frac{1}{n}\sum_{i=1}^{n} x_i\right\} = \frac{1}{n}\sum_{i=1}^{n} E[x_i] = \frac{1}{n}\sum_{i=1}^{n} m = \frac{1}{n}nm = m$$

Problem 5-2

$$E(s_x^2) = E\left\{\frac{1}{n-1}\sum_{i=1}^{n}(x_i - \bar{x})^2\right\}$$

$$= \frac{1}{n-1}E\left\{\sum_{i=1}^{n}(x_i - \bar{x})^2\right\}$$

$$= \frac{1}{n-1}\sum_{i=1}^{n} E[(x_i - \bar{x})^2]$$

$$= \frac{1}{n-1}\sum_{i=1}^{n}\left\{E[x_i^2] - m^2\right\}$$

$$= \frac{1}{n-1}\sum_{i=1}^{n} var(x_i) = \frac{n}{n-1}var(x_i)$$

Problem 5-3

The sum of all the gains is 975. Hence the sample mean is $975/10 = 97.5$. The sum of the squares of all the gains is 97,339. Thus, from (5-5), the sample standard deviation is

$$s_x = \sqrt{\frac{10(97,339) - (975)^2}{9(10)}} = 15.904$$

Problem 5-4

Start with (5-13) and (5-14):

$$\left(\sum x_i^2\right)\alpha_0 + \left(\sum x_i\right)\beta_0 = \sum x_i y_i \quad (1)$$

$$\left(\sum x_i\right)\alpha_0 + n\beta_0 = \sum y_i \quad (2)$$

where all sums are assumed to be from 1 to n. From (1):

$$\beta_0 = \frac{\sum x_i y_i - \alpha_0 \sum x_i^2}{\sum x_i}$$

Substitute into (2):

$$\left(\sum x_i\right)\alpha_0 + n\frac{\sum x_i y_i - \alpha_0 \sum x_i^2}{\sum x_i} = \sum y_i$$

Solve for α_0:

$$\alpha_0\left(\sum x_i - n\frac{\sum x_i^2}{\sum x_i}\right) = \sum y_i - n\frac{\sum x_i y_i}{\sum x_i}$$

or

$$\alpha_0 = \frac{n\sum x_i y_i - \sum x_i \sum y_i}{n(n-1)\left(\dfrac{n\sum x_i^2 - \left(\sum x_i\right)^2}{n(n-1)}\right)} = \frac{n\sum x_i y_i - \sum x_i \sum y_i}{n(n-1)s_x^2}$$

where (5-5) has been used to substitute for s_x^2.

Problem 5-5

The definition, of the sample means of $\{x_i\}$ and $\{y_i\}$ are

$$\bar{x} = \frac{1}{n}\sum x_i \text{ and } \bar{y} = \frac{1}{n}\sum y_i$$

where all sums are assumed to be from 1 to n. By definition

$$c_{xy} = \frac{1}{n-1}\sum (x_i - \bar{x})(y_i - \bar{y})$$

$$= \frac{1}{n-1}\sum (x_i y_i - \bar{x}y_i - \bar{y}x_i + \bar{x}\,\bar{y})$$

$$= \frac{1}{n-1}\left[\sum x_i y_i - \bar{x}\sum y_i - \bar{y}\sum x_i + n\bar{x}\,\bar{y}\right]$$

$$= \frac{1}{n-1}\left[\sum x_i y_i - \bar{x}(n\bar{y}) - \bar{y}(n\bar{x}) + n\bar{x}\,\bar{y}\right]$$

$$= \frac{1}{n-1}\left[\sum x_i y_i - n\bar{x}\,\bar{y}\right] = \frac{1}{n(n-1)}\left[n\sum x_i y_i - n^2\bar{x}\,\bar{y}\right]$$

$$= \frac{n\sum x_i y_i - \sum x_i{}_{y_i}}{n(n-1)}$$

Problem 5-6

Rewrite (5-20) as

$$y - \bar{y} = \frac{c_{xy}}{s_x s_y}\frac{s_y}{s_x}(x - \bar{x})$$

Divide both sides by s_y and use the definition of r_{xy}:

$$\frac{y - \bar{y}}{s_y} = \frac{c_{xy}}{s_x s_y}\frac{x - \bar{x}}{s_x} = r_{xy}\frac{x - \bar{x}}{s_x}$$

Problem 5-7

The $\{x_i\}$ and $\{y_i\}$ are linearly related:

$$y_i = mx_i + b \text{ and } \bar{y} = m\bar{x} + b$$

By definition

$$s_y^2 = \frac{1}{n-1}\sum (y_i - \bar{y})^2$$

where the sum is from $i = 1$ to n. Substitute for y_i and $\bar{y}$:

$$s_y^2 = \frac{1}{n-1}\sum (mx_i + b - m\bar{x} - b)^2 = m^2\frac{1}{n-1}\sum (x_i - \bar{x})^2 = m^2 s_x^2$$

Also, by definition

$$c_{xy} = \frac{1}{n-1}\sum (x_i - \bar{x})(y_i - \bar{y})^2$$

$$= \frac{1}{n-1}\sum (x_i - \bar{x})(mx_i - m\bar{x})$$

$$= \frac{m}{n-1}\sum (x_i - \bar{x})^2 = m s_x^2$$

Now

$$r_{xy} = \frac{c_{xy}}{s_x s_y} = \frac{m s_x^2}{s_x\sqrt{m^2 s_x^2}} = \frac{m s_x^2}{\pm m s_x^2} = \pm 1$$

This is (5-24). For (5-25), consider

$$\frac{1}{n-1}\sum \left[\frac{x_i - \bar{x}}{s_x} \pm \frac{y_i - \bar{y}}{s_y} \right]^2 \geq 0$$

which is greater than or equal to zero because each term in the sum is nonnegative. This can be expanded to give

59

$$\frac{1}{s_x^2} \frac{1}{n-1} \sum (x_i - \bar{x})^2 \pm \frac{2}{s_x s_y} \frac{1}{n-1} \sum (x_i - \bar{x})(y_i - \bar{y}) + \frac{1}{s_y^2} \frac{1}{n-1} \sum (y_i - \bar{y})^2 \geq 0$$

Use definitions of s_x^2, s_y^2, and c_{xy} to get

$$\frac{s_x^2}{s_x^2} \pm \frac{2}{s_x s_y} c_{xy} + \frac{s_y^2}{s_y^2} \geq 0$$

or

$$1 \pm 2r_{xy} + 1 \geq 0$$

Using the + sign and then the - sign, and solving the inequality we have

$$r_{xy} \leq 1 \quad \text{and} \quad r_{xy} \geq -1$$

Problem 5-8

A MATLAB program for doing the regression analysis is given below:

```
clg
x = [0.77 4.39 4.11 2.91 0.56 0.89 4.09 2.38 0.78 2.52];
y = [14.62 22.21 20.12 19.42 14.69 15.23 24.48 16.88 8.56 16.24];
mx = mean(x);
my = mean(y);
sx = std(x);
sy = std(y);
rxy = corrcoef(x, y);
disp(' ')
fprintf('The sample means of {x} & {y} are %5.2f and %5.2f, respectively\n',mx,my)
fprintf('The sample std deviations of {x} & {y} are %5.2f and %5.2f, respectively\n',sx,sy)
fprintf('The sample correlation coefficient of {x} & {y} is %5.2f\n',rxy(1,2))
disp(' ')
xv = 0:0.1:5;
yv = rxy(1,2)*sy*(xv - mx)/sx + my;
plot(xv, yv, 'w'), grid, xlabel('xi'),ylabel('yi')
hold
plot(x, y, '+w')
print c:\probab\new\prob5_8 -dps
```

» pr5_8
The sample means of {x} & {y} are 2.34 and 17.24, respectively
The sample std deviations of {x} & {y} are 1.52 and 4.52, respectively
The sample correlation coefficient of {x} & {y} is 0.87

A plot of the data
and regression
line are shown
below:

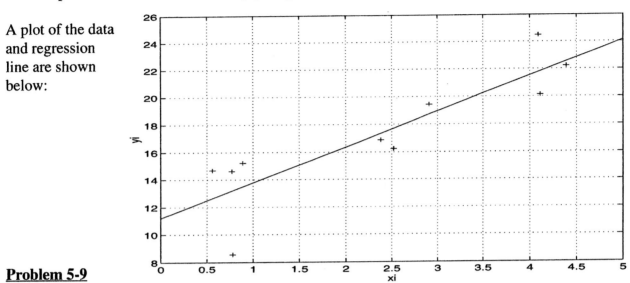

Problem 5-9

Except for the data, the MATLAB program is the same as for Problem 5-8. A plot is given
below for the regression line and the data.

» pr5_9
The sample means of {x} & {y} are 2.34 and 6.37, respectively
The sample std
deviations of {x} &
{y} are 1.52 and
3.18, respectively
The sample
correlation
coefficient of {x}
& {y} is 0.02

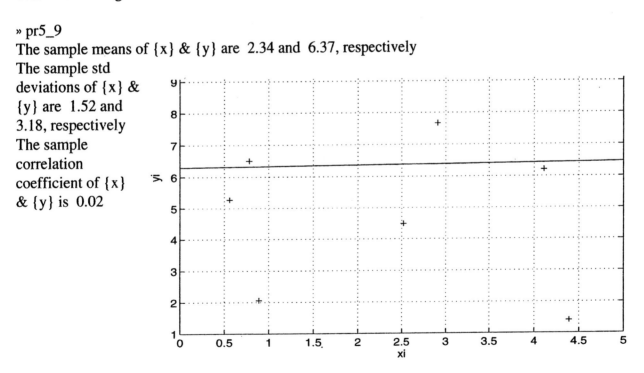

Problem 5-10

The program is the same as Problem 5-8 except that the natural log of the y-data is taken.

```
clg
x = [1.14 4.55 7.52 6.86 5.43 0.74 4.37 2.02 6.96 2.90];
y = [10.61 190.6 3702 1914 464.5 5.79 162.7 24.7 2118 45.7];
z = log(y);
mx = mean(x);
mz = mean(z);
sx = std(x);
sz = std(z);
rxz = corrcoef(x, z);
disp(' ')
fprintf('The sample means of {x} & {log y} are %5.2f and %5.2f, respectively\n',mx,mz)
fprintf('The sample std deviations of {x} & {log y} are %5.2f and %5.2f, respectively\n',sx,sz)
fprintf('The sample correlation coefficient of {x} & {log y} is %5.2f\n',rxz(1,2))
disp(' ')
xv = 0:0.1:8;
zv = rxz(1,2)*sz*(xv - mx)/sx + mz;
plot(xv, zv, 'w'), grid, xlabel('xi'),ylabel('log yi')
hold
plot(x, z, '+w')
print c:\probab\new\prob5_10 -dps
```

```
» pr5_10
 The sample means of {x} & {log y} are  4.25 and  5.11, respectively
The sample std deviations of {x} & {log y} are  2.48 and  2.29, respectively
The sample correlation coefficient of {x} & {log y} is  1.00
```

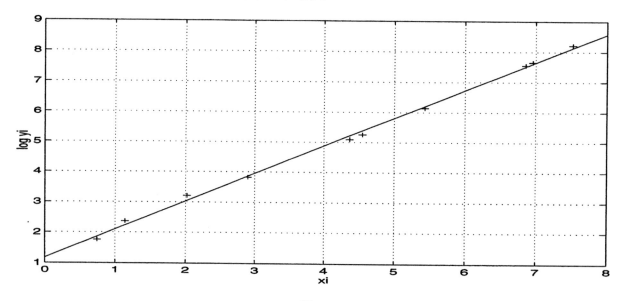

Problem 5-11

A MATLAB program and plot of the empirical cdf is given below:

```
clg
gain = [112 77 113 83 95 105 102 120 73 95];
gain_inc = sort(gain);
L = length(gain);
J = 1:1:L;
J_norm = J/L;
[xb, yb] = stairs(gain_inc, J_norm);
plot(xb, yb, 'w'), grid, xlabel('gain'),ylabel('fraction <= abscissa'),...
        axis([60 130 0 1])
print c:\probab\new\prob5_11 -dps
```

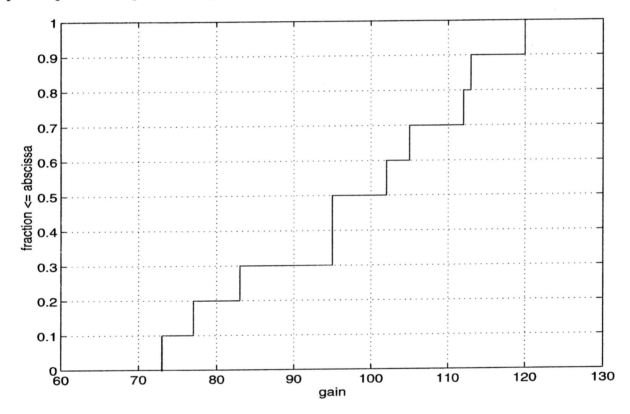

Problem 5-12

The MATLAB program is the same as for Problem 5-11 except for the data sets. Plots for the
empirical cdf's are given on the next page.

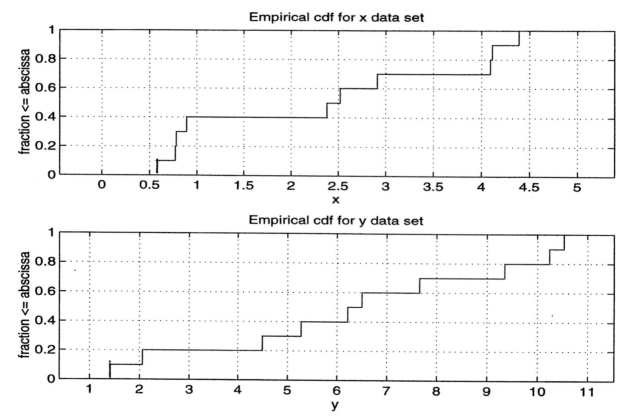

Problem 5-13

β = {112, 77, 113, 83, 95, 105, 102, 120, 73, 95}. The sample mean is 97.5 from Problem 5-3. Lot means are

$$\overline{x}_1 = \frac{112 + 77 + 113}{3} = 100.67$$

$$\overline{x}_2 = \frac{83 + 95 + 105}{3} = 94.33$$

$$\overline{x}_3 = \frac{102 + 120 + 73}{3} = 98.33$$

The sample standard deviation of the lot means is 3.257. The upper and lower control limits are

$$UCL = 97.5 + 3(3.257) = 107.27$$

$$and \ LCL = 97.5 - 3(3.257) = 87.73$$

respectively. None of the lot means are outside of the control limits; the process is in control.

Problem 5-14

In (5-30) we let

$$\beta = \frac{k\sigma_X}{\sqrt{n}} \quad \text{and} \quad \frac{1}{k^2} = \frac{\sigma_X^2}{n\beta^2} = \alpha$$

so that (5-30) becomes

$$P\left[\left|\frac{1}{n}\sum x_i - \mu_X\right| \geq \beta\right] \leq \alpha$$

We have

$$\alpha = \frac{1}{n\beta^2} = \frac{1}{100\beta^2}$$

A table of α versus β is given below:

β	α
0.01	100
0.1	1
0.3	0.111
0.5	0.04

CHAPTER 6
ESTIMATION THEORY AND APPLICATIONS

Problem 6-1

(a) Order the data values: 1.0, 2.0, 6.8, 7.1, 8.4, 9.4, 10.3, 10.4, 10.7, 10.9, 12.8, 13.4, 13.6. The middle datum is 10.3, which in this case is the median. The sample mean is 8.99. In this case, they differ by about 10%.

(b) If the datum 1000 is appended, the median is between 10.3 and 10.4, call it 10.35. The sample mean now becomes 79.77. Thus the median is a much more stable estimate of the "typical" datum.

Problem 6-2

(a) From (6-8)

$$\text{MSE} = \text{var}(\hat{\theta}) + B^2 = 4 + 2^2 = 8$$

(b) Again, from (6-8) rearranged

$$\text{var}(\hat{\theta}) = \text{MSE} - B^2 = 10 - 9 = 1$$

The standard deviation is also 1.

Problem 6-3

From (6-9)

$$\text{var}(\bar{x}) = \frac{\text{var}(\{x_i\})}{n} \quad \text{or} \quad \text{var}(\{x_i\}) = n\,\text{var}(\bar{x}) = 10(10^2) = 1000$$

We want

$$\text{var}(\bar{x}) = (0.1)^2 = \frac{1000}{n}$$

Therefore $n = 1000/(0.1^2) = 100{,}000$ samples.

Problem 6-4

The definition of the empirical cdf is

$$\tilde{F}_X(x \mid x_1, x_2, \cdots, x_n) = \frac{\text{number of samples } x_1, x_2, \cdots, x_n \leq x}{n}$$

Thus, the estimate for the median is defined by

$$\tilde{F}_X(\hat{m} \mid x_1, x_2, \cdots, x_n) = 0.5$$

or

$$\frac{\text{number of samples } x_1, x_2, \cdots, x_n \leq \hat{m}}{n} = 0.5$$

or

$$\text{number of samples } x_1, x_2, \cdots, x_n \leq \hat{m} = 0.5n$$

This is the definition of the median, which is that half the samples $(0.5n)$ lie below the median and half above the median.

Problem 6-5

First consider $a < m$. Look at $E(|X - m|)$. Since $|x - m| = x - m$ for $x > m$ and $|x - m| = m - x$ for $x < m$, we have

$$E(|X - m|) = \int_m^\infty x f_X(x)dx - \int_{-\infty}^m x f_X(x)dx + m\left[\int_{-\infty}^m f_X(x)dx - \int_m^\infty f_X(x)dx\right]$$

Similarly

$$E(|X - a|) = \int_a^{\infty} x f_X(x)dx - \int_{-\infty}^a x f_X(x)dx + a\left[\int_{-\infty}^a f_X(x)dx - \int_a^{\infty} f_X(x)dx\right]$$

$$= \int_a^m x f_X(x)dx + \int_m^{\infty} x f_X(x)dx - \left[\int_{-\infty}^m x f_X(x)dx - \int_a^m x f_X(x)dx\right]$$

$$+ a\left[\int_{-\infty}^a f_X(x)dx - \int_a^{\infty} f_X(x)dx\right] + m\left[\int_{-\infty}^m f_X(x)dx - \int_m^{\infty} f_X(x)dx\right]$$

$$- m\left[\int_{-\infty}^m f_X(x)dx - \int_m^{\infty} f_X(x)dx\right]$$

Comparing this with the expression for E(|X - m|), we see that

$$E(|X - a|) = E(|X - m|) + 2\int_a^m (x - a)f_X(x)dx + (a - m)\left[\int_{-\infty}^m f_X(x)dx - \int_m^{\infty} f_X(x)dx\right]$$

The bracketed term at the end is zero by definition of the median. Thus the case for $a < m$ is proved. The case for $a > m$ is proved similarly.

In the final expression for $a < m$ note that the integral

$$2\int_a^m (x - a)f_X(x)dx$$

is positive because $f_X(x)$ is nonnegative and $x \geq a$ inside the integral. Hence, for $a < m$, it has been proved that E(|X - a|) is smallest if $a = m$. A similar observation holds for the case $a > m$.

Problem 6-6

The estimator in question is

$$\hat{\sigma}_x^2 = \frac{1}{n-1}\sum_{i=1}^n (x_i - \hat{\mu}_x)^2 \quad \text{where} \quad \hat{\mu}_x = \frac{1}{n}\sum_{i=1}^n x_i$$

Taking the expectation of the estimator for the variance, we have

$$E(\hat{\sigma}_x^2) = \frac{1}{n-1}\sum_{i=1}^{n} E[(x_i - \hat{\mu}_x)^2]$$

$$= \frac{1}{n-1}\sum_{i=1}^{n} E[x_i^2 - 2\hat{\mu}_x x_i + \hat{\mu}_x^2]$$

$$= \frac{1}{n-1}\sum_{i=1}^{n} \{E[x_i^2] - 2E[\hat{\mu}_x x_i] + E[\hat{\mu}_x^2]\}$$

As intermediate steps, consider

$$E(\hat{\mu}_x x_i) = \frac{1}{n}\sum_{j=1}^{n} E(x_j x_i) = \begin{cases} \dfrac{1}{n}\sum_{j=1}^{n} E(x_i^2) = \sigma_x^2 + \mu_x^2, & i = j \\[2ex] \dfrac{1}{n}\sum_{j=1}^{n} E^2(x_i) = (n-1)\mu_x^2, & i \neq j \end{cases}$$

where μ_x is the mean of the x_i's and σ_x^2 is their common variance. Also

$$E(\hat{\mu}_x^2) = E\left[\left(\frac{1}{n}\sum_{i=1}^{n} x_i\right)^2\right]$$

$$= \frac{1}{n^2}\sum_{i=1}^{n}\sum_{j=1}^{n} E(x_i x_j)$$

$$= \begin{cases} \dfrac{1}{n^2}\sum_i \sum_j E(x_i^2), & i = j \\[2ex] \dfrac{1}{n^2}\sum_i \sum_j E(x_i)E(x_j) = \, , & i \neq j \end{cases}$$

$$= \frac{1}{n}[\sigma_x^2 + \mu_x^2 + (n-1)\mu_x^2]$$

Putting this all into the equation at the top of the page (the expectation of the estimator), we obtain

69

$$E(\sigma_x^2) = \frac{1}{n-1}\{n(\sigma_x^2 + \mu_x^2) - 2[(\sigma_x^2 + \mu_x^2) + (n-1)\mu_x^2]$$

$$+ [\sigma_x^2 + \mu_x^2 + (n-1)\mu_x^2]\} = \sigma_x^2$$

Problem 6-7

We want to show that

$$E[\hat{C}(X, Y)] = E[(X - \mu_X)(Y - \mu_Y)] = E(XY) - \mu_X \mu_Y$$

Thus, consider

$$n(n-1)E[\hat{C}(X, Y)] = nE\left[\sum_{i=1}^{n} X_i Y_i\right] - E\left[\sum_{i=1}^{n} X_i \sum_{j=1}^{n} Y_j\right]$$

$$= n\sum_{i=1}^{n} E(X_i Y_i) - \sum_{i=1}^{n}\sum_{j=1}^{n} E(X_i Y_j)$$

Because all samples are identically distributed (i.e., from the same population), we have

$$E(X_i Y_i) = m_{11}, \text{ all } i \text{ and } E(X_i Y_j) = m_{11}, i = j, \text{ and } E(X_i Y_j) = \mu_X \mu_Y, i \neq j$$

where μ_X and μ_Y are the means of the X_i's and Y_j's, respectively. Substituting, we obtain

$$n(n-1)E[\hat{C}(X, Y)] = n(n-1)m_{11} - n(n-1)\mu_X \mu_Y$$

or

$$E[\hat{C}(X, Y)] = m_{11} - \mu_X \mu_Y = E(XY) - E(X)E(Y)$$

Problem 6-8

Neither is totally satisfactory. The median = \$15,000 is biased toward the lower end, and the sample mean = \$30,926 is biased toward the upper end. Without the owner, the sample mean is \$20,577 which is more representative of the typical salary.

Problem 6-9

The number of customers in T minutes is approximately λT (this is the expected number of customers), so take the estimate for λ as

$$\hat{\lambda} = \frac{\text{number of customers in } T \text{ minutes}}{T}$$

Problem 6-10

The maximum likelihood estimate must satisfy

$$\frac{\partial P_T(k, \lambda)}{\partial \lambda} = \frac{k(\lambda T)^{k-1}T}{k!}e^{-\lambda T} + \frac{(\lambda T)^k}{k!}(-T)e^{-\lambda T} = 0$$

This reduces to

$$\frac{k}{\lambda} - T = 0 \text{ or } \hat{\lambda} = \frac{k}{T}$$

We can show that this indeed provides a maximum.

Problem 6-11

The number of heads obeys a binomial distribution. Thus let

$$P(\text{no. of heads} = k) = \binom{100}{k} p^k (1-p)^{100-k} = \Lambda(p)$$

Differentiate with respect to p and set the result equal to zero (a necessary condition for the maximum likelihood estimate):

$$\frac{\partial \Lambda(p)}{\partial p} = \binom{100}{k}\left[kp^{k-1}(1-p)^{100-k} - p^k(100-k)(1-p)^{100-k-1}\right]$$

Setting this equal to zero, the condition for the maximum likelihood estimate is

$$k\hat{p}^{k-1}(1-\hat{p})^{100-k} = \hat{p}^k(100-k)(1-\hat{p})^{100-k-1}$$

71

When solved, this gives

$$\hat{p} = \frac{k}{100} = \frac{\text{number of heads observed in an experiment}}{100}$$

The estimates for p from the 10 experiments according to this estimator are 0.57, 0.63, 0.59, 0.70, 0.65, 0.52, 0.61, 0.49, 0.55, and 0.67. The estimates appear to be biased above 0.5.
(b) The sample mean of the estimates for p is 0.598.
(c) The sample variance is

$$\hat{\sigma}_x^2 = \frac{1}{9}\sum_{i=1}^{10}(\hat{p}_i - 0.598)^2 = 0.00448$$

The sample standard deviation is

$$\hat{\sigma} = 0.06697$$

Problem 6-12

$E(\text{number of heads}) = np = 100p$ using the result for the mean of a binomial random variable. Thus

$$E(\hat{p}) = \frac{1}{100}E(\text{number of heads}) = p$$

So the estimator is unbiased (its expectation equals the quantity being estimated). The variance of the number of heads is $npq = 100pq$ where $q = 1-p$ using the result for the variance of a binomial random variable. Thus

$$\text{var}(\hat{p}) = \frac{1}{(100)^2}(100pq) = \frac{pq}{100} = \frac{p(1-p)}{100}$$

Problem 6-13

The expectation of the estimator of (6-22), from problem 6-6, is σ_x^2. Note that

$$\hat{\sigma}_{X,(6-20b)}^2 = \frac{n-1}{n}\hat{\sigma}_{X,(6-22)}^2$$

Hence

$$E[\hat{\sigma}^2_{X,\,(6\text{-}20b)}] \;=\; \frac{n-1}{n}E[\hat{\sigma}^2_{X,\,(6\text{-}22)}] \;=\; \frac{n-1}{n}\sigma^2_X$$

Thus

$$\text{bias of }(6\text{-}20b) \;=\; \sigma^2_X - \frac{n-1}{n}\sigma^2_X \;=\; \frac{1}{n}\sigma^2_X$$

Problem 6-14

MATLAB programs for carrying out the calculations and plotting the empirical cdf's are given below:

```
%        Solution for 6-14: sample mean
%
%
step_size = 0.005;
nn = 1/step_size;
samp_mean = [10.24 9.32 11.44 9.65 10.98 10.03 9.72 10.01 10.39 9.84];
s_mean_mean = mean(samp_mean);
s_var_mean = std(samp_mean)^2;
sort_sa_mean = sort(samp_mean);
n = length(sort_sa_mean);
x = zeros(1, nn*n);
y_sa_mean = zeros(1, nn*n);
ys_sa_mean = zeros(1, nn*n);
ys_gauss = zeros(1, nn*n);
x(1) = min(sort_sa_mean)-1;
for p = 1:n
        for i = 1:nn*n-1
                x(i+1) = x(i)+step_size;
                if x(i+1) >= sort_sa_mean(p) & x(i) < sort_sa_mean(p)
                        y_sa_mean(i+1) = y_sa_mean(i)+1;
                end
                if i > 1
                ys_sa_mean(i+1) = ys_sa_mean(i) + y_sa_mean(i+1);
                inc(i) = exp(-(x(i)-s_mean_mean)^2/(2*s_var_mean))/sqrt(2*pi*s_var_mean);
                ys_gauss(i+1) = ys_gauss(i) + inc(i)*step_size;
                end
        end
end
ys_sa_mean = ys_sa_mean/max(ys_sa_mean);
```

```
plot(x, ys_sa_mean,'w'),xlabel('x'), ylabel('empirical cdf'),...
title('Comparison of empirical cdf of sample mean of 10 batches of 100 samples with Gaussian')
hold
plot(x, ys_gauss,'--w')
print c:\probab\new\pr_14a -dps
```

The program for sample variance is similar. Plots of the empirical and analytical Gaussian cdf's are shown below. The empirical and Gaussian cdf's are closest for the sample mean as one would expect.

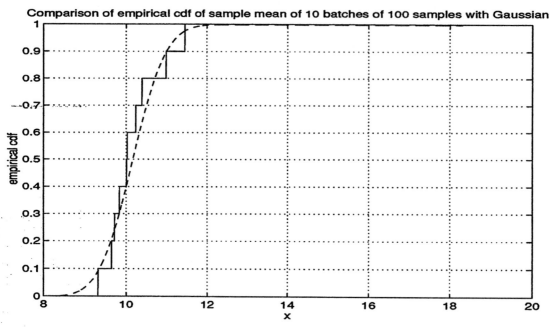

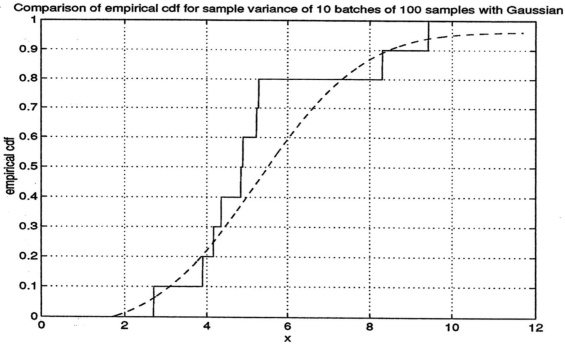

Problem 6-15

(a) The sample mean is 15.89; (b) The expectation of the sample mean is the mean of the population which was given as 15. The variance of the sample mean is the variance for the population divided by the number of samples, or $9/10 = 0.9$.

Problem 6-16

The 95% confidence interval for the mean obeys

$$P(-v_c < \sqrt{n}(\alpha - \mu_X)/\sigma_X < v_c) = 0.95 = 1 - \alpha$$

As discussed in the text, we split the area under the tails of the pdf for the sample mean between the positive and negative tails. From (6-27), this is

$$P(\bar{x} > v_c) = 0.25 = Q\left(\frac{\sqrt{n}\beta}{\sigma_X}\right)$$

From a table of Q-function values, we find that

$$\frac{\sqrt{n}\beta}{\sigma_X} = 1.96$$

so for $n = 10$ and $\sigma_X^2 = 9$, we have

$$\beta = \frac{3(1.96)}{\sqrt{10}} = 1.85$$

Thus

$$P(\bar{x} - \beta < \mu_X < \bar{x} + \beta) = 0.95 \text{ or } P(14.04 < \mu_X < 17.74) = 0.95$$

Problem 6-17

From (6-40)

$$P\left(\frac{n\hat{\sigma}_X^2}{\delta} < \sigma_X^2 < \frac{n\hat{\sigma}_X^2}{\gamma}\right) = 1 - \alpha = 0.95$$

From Example 6-5, $\delta = 20.483$ and $\gamma = 3.247$. We need the sample variance, mean known, which can be calculated to be

$$\hat{\sigma}_X^2 = \frac{1}{10}\sum_{i=1}^{10}(x_i - \mu_X)^2$$

$$= \frac{1}{10}\sum_{i=1}^{10}[(8.81 - 15)^2 + (15.91 - 15)^2 + (20.39 - 15)^2 + (8.63 - 15)^2 + (13.8 - 15)^2$$

$$+ (21.73 - 15)^2 + (27.23 - 15)^2 + (7.32 - 15)^2 + (14.83 - 15)^2 + (20.26 - 15)^2]$$

$$= 39.18$$

Therefore, the above expression becomes

$$P\left(\frac{10(39.18)}{20.483} < \sigma_X^2 < \frac{10(39.18)}{3.247}\right) = 1 - \alpha = 0.95$$

or

$$P\left(19.13 < \sigma_X^2 < 120.65\right) = 0.95$$

Problem 6-18

The confidence interval is defined as

$$P\left(\frac{(n-1)\hat{\sigma}_X^2}{\delta} < \sigma_X^2 < \frac{(n-1)\hat{\sigma}_X^2}{\gamma}\right) = 1 - \alpha = 0.95$$

The sample variance, mean unknown, can be calculated to be 42.647. We found $\gamma = 2.7$ and δ 19.023 in Example 6-6 for 9 degrees of freedom. Putting the numbers into the above formula, we obtain $P[20.18 < \sigma_X^2 < 142.16] = 0.95$.

Problem 6-19

From (6-48b) we have

$$T = \frac{Z}{\sqrt{W/(n-1)}} = \frac{\sqrt{n}(\hat{\mu}_X - \mu_X)}{\hat{\sigma}_X} \sim \text{Student's T distribution}$$

The confidence interval is specified by

$$P(-t_c < T < t_c) = 1 - \alpha = 0.95$$

From Example 6-7, we have $t_c = 2.263$ for $1 - \alpha = 0.95$. From Problem 6-18, we know that the sample standard deviation is $(42.647)^{1/2} = 6.53$. Thus the confidence interval obeys

$$P\left[-2.263 < \frac{\sqrt{10}(15.89 - \mu_X)}{6.53} < 2.263\right] = 0.95$$

Solving for the standard deviation, we obtain

$$P(11.22 < \mu_X < 20.56) = 0.95$$

as the confidence interval for 95% confidence.

Problem 6-20

From (6-55b)

$$P(p - \beta < \bar{x} = k/n < p + \beta) = 1 - \alpha$$

(a) From Example 6-8, $\beta = 0.0435$ form 95% confidence. From the given data, $\bar{x} = 260/500 = 0.52$.

$$P(p - 0.0435 < 0.52 < p + 0.0435) = 0.95$$

Solving for p, we obtain

$$P(0.52 - 0.0435 < p < 0.52 + 0.0435) = 0.95 \text{ or } P(0.477 < p < 0.564) = 0.95$$

(b) Now $\bar{x} = 475/500 = 0.95$. The confidence interval is specified by

$$P(0.95 - 0.0435 < p < 0.95 + 0.0435) = 0.95 \text{ or } P(0.907 < p < 0.994) = 0.95$$

Problem 6-21

For a Poisson random variable

$$P(k) = \frac{(\lambda T)^k}{k!} e^{-\lambda T}$$

the expected value is $E(K) = \lambda T$. Therefore, the expected value of the estimator for λ is

$$E(\hat{\lambda}) = E(K/T) = \frac{1}{T}E(K) = \frac{\lambda T}{T} = \lambda$$

Since the expected value of the estimator is equal to the quantity being estimated, the estimator is unbiased.

To see if its efficient, we attempt to apply (6-60). Rewrite the distribution as

$$P(k) = \frac{1}{k!} e^{-\lambda T} e^{\ln[(\lambda T)^k]} = \frac{1}{k!} e^{-\lambda T + k[\ln(\lambda) + \ln(T)]}$$

which is of the form (6-60), so the maximum likelihood estimator is efficient.

Problem 6-22

The pdf of the estimator for the variance, mean known, is Chi-square with n degrees of freedom. This pdf is given by (6-36) for a single random variable. For n independent samples, the joint pdf of the samples is

$$f_{\bar{X}}(x_1, x_2, \cdots, x_n) = \prod_{i=1}^{n} \frac{x_i^{\frac{n}{2}-1} e^{-x_i/2}}{\Gamma(n/2)2^{n/2}}$$

$$= \prod_{i=1}^{n} \frac{e^{-x_i/2} e^{\ln[x_i^{\frac{n}{2}-1}]}}{\Gamma(n/2)2^{n/2}}$$

$$= \frac{e^{-\sum_{i=1}^{n}[x_i/2 - (n/2 - 1)\ln x_i]}}{\sqrt{2}\Gamma^n(n/2)}$$

which is of the form (6-60), so the maximum likelihood estimator is efficient.

Problem 6-23

(a) The conditional pdf is

$$f_{H|W} = f_\Delta(\delta = h - w/16) = \frac{e^{-(h-w/16)^2/0.4}}{\sqrt{0.4\pi}}$$

(b) From (6-69)

$$\text{mmse estimate} = E[H|w] = \int_{-\infty}^{\infty} h \frac{e^{-(h-w/16)^2/0.4}}{\sqrt{0.4\pi}} dh$$

The integral is the expression for $E(H)$ where $E(H) = w/16$. So, for a 90 pound student, the mmse estimate of his/her height is $90/16 = 5.625$ feet.

(c) The mean-square error is

$$\text{mean-square error} = \int_{-\infty}^{\infty} \left(h - \frac{w}{16}\right)^2 \frac{e^{-(h-w/16)^2/0.4}}{\sqrt{0.4\pi}} dh$$

$$= \text{variance of the Gaussian pdf} = 0.2$$

The root-mean-square error is $(0.2)^{1/2} = 0.447$ feet.

Problem 6-24

Use the expression for the total variance given by (6-74):

$$\frac{1}{\sigma_p^2} = \frac{n}{\sigma_n^2} + \frac{1}{\sigma_Y^2} = \frac{1}{1}$$

Since $\sigma_Y^2 = 5$ and $\sigma_n^2 = 25$, we can calculate n to be

$$n = 25\left(1 - \frac{1}{5}\right) = 25(4/5) = 20$$

The conditional mean estimate is

$$E(Y \mid x) = \frac{n\sigma_Y^2/\sigma_n^2}{1 + n\sigma_Y^2/\sigma_n^2}\bar{x} + \frac{1}{1 + n\sigma_Y^2/\sigma_n^2}m_Y = \frac{4}{5}\bar{x} + \frac{1}{5}m_Y = \frac{4}{5}\bar{x} + 2$$

so its more dependent on the sample mean.

Problem 6-25

The two orthogonality relationships suggested in the problem statement are

$$E\{[Y - (AX + B)]\} = 0 \quad (1)$$

$$E\{[Y - (AX + B)]X\} = 0 \quad (2)$$

(2) becomes

$$E(XY) - AE(X^2) - BE(X) = 0 \quad \text{or} \quad -3 - 5A - 2B = 0$$

and (1) becomes

$$E(Y) - AE(X) - B = 0 \quad \text{or} \quad 1 - 2A - B = 0$$

Solve and find that $A = -5$ and $B = 11$. So the estimator is

$$\theta(X) = -5X + 11$$

CHAPTER 7
ENGINEERING DECISIONS

Problem 7-1

(a) From (7-12)

$$\Lambda(Z) = \frac{f_Z(Z \mid H_1)}{f_Z(Z \mid H_0)} = \frac{e^{-(z-10)^2/32} \sqrt{32\pi}}{\sqrt{32\pi} \; e^{-z^2/32}} = e^{(20z-100)/32} = e^{0.625z-3.125}$$

(b) From the right-hand side of (7-12)

$$\text{threshold} = \frac{p(c_{10} - c_{00})}{q(c_{01} - c_{11})} = \frac{\frac{1}{3}(15-1)}{\frac{2}{3}(5-2)} = 2.333$$

(c) The hypothesis test is

$$e^{0.625Z - 3.125} \overset{H_1}{\underset{H_0}{\gtrless}} 2.333$$

Taking the natural logarithm of both sides, this can be reduced to

$$Z \overset{H_1}{\underset{H_0}{\gtrless}} \frac{\ln(2.333) + 3.125}{0.625} = 6.355$$

Problem 7-2

The likelihood ratio is

$$\Lambda(Z) = \frac{f_Z(Z \mid H_1)}{f_Z(Z \mid H_0)} = \frac{\frac{1}{10}[u(Z) - u)Z - 10)]}{10e^{-10Z}u(Z)} = \begin{cases} \dfrac{e^{10Z}}{100}, & 0 \le Z \le 10 \\ \\ 0, & \text{otherwise} \end{cases}$$

The theshold is 1. Hence the Bayes' test is

$$e^{10Z} \underset{H_0}{\overset{H_1}{\underset{<}{>}}} 100 \text{ or } Z \underset{H_0}{\overset{H_1}{\underset{<}{>}}} \ln(100)/10 = 0.4605$$

From (7-10), the average cost is

$$C(D) = \frac{1}{2} + \int_0^{0.4605} \frac{1}{2}\frac{1}{10}dz - \int_0^{0.4605} \frac{1}{2}(10)e^{-10z}dz = 0.028$$

Problem 7-3

The likelihood ratio is

$$\Lambda(Z) = \frac{f_Z(Z \mid H_1)}{f_Z(Z \mid H_0)} = \frac{e^{-|Z|}}{2}\frac{\sqrt{8\pi}}{e^{-Z^2/8}} = \sqrt{2\pi}\,e^{Z^2/8 - |Z|}$$

The threshold is 1. The likelihood ratio test can be reduced to

$$\frac{Z^2}{8} - |Z| \underset{H_0}{\overset{H_1}{\underset{<}{>}}} -\frac{1}{2}\ln(2\pi) \text{ or } Z^2 - 8|Z| \underset{H_0}{\overset{H_1}{\underset{<}{>}}} -4\ln(2\pi) = -7.352$$

To determine decision boundaries, solve

$$Z_0^2 - 8|Z_0| + 7.352 = 0$$

first assuming $Z_0 > 0$, in which case $|Z_0| = Z_0$, and then assuming $Z_0 < 0$, in which case $|Z_0| = -Z_0$. We find the boundary points to be at

$$Z_0 = \pm\frac{8 \pm \sqrt{64 - 4(7.352)}}{2} = -6.941, -1.059, 1.059, 6.941$$

That is, for $Z < -6.941$ we choose H_1, for $-6.941 \le Z < -1.059$ we choose H_0, for $-1.059 \le Z < 1.059$ we choose H_1, for $1.059 \le Z < 6.941$ we choose H_0, and for $Z \ge 6.941$ we choose H_1. Note that the $\le$ and $<$ signs can be on either end of the interval because the random variables are continuous.

The average cost, from (7-10), is

$$C(D) = \frac{1}{2}(1) + \frac{1}{2}(0) + 2\int_{1.059}^{6.941}\left(\frac{1}{2}(1)\frac{1}{2}e^{-|z|} - \frac{1}{2}(1)\frac{e^{-z^2/8}}{\sqrt{8\pi}}\right)dz$$

where the 2 in front of the integral is because of the eveness of the integrand. Carrying out the integration gives

$$C(D) = \frac{1}{2} - \frac{1}{2}\left[e^{-6.941} - e^{-1.0598}\right] - \left[Q\left(\frac{1.059}{2}\right) - Q\left(\frac{6.941}{2}\right)\right] = 0.375$$

Problem 7-4

The critical region boundary is given by

$$c = Q^{-1}(\alpha/2) = Q^{-1}(0.025) = 1.96$$

From Example 7-6, we have $\bar{x} = 9.962$ and $Y = -1.202$. Since $-c < Y < c$ we accept the hypothesis that the bar is 10 cm long at the 95% significance level. The OC curve is given by

$$\beta(\mu) = 1 - Q\left(c - \frac{\mu - \mu_0}{\sigma/\sqrt{n}}\right) - Q\left(c + \frac{\mu - \mu_0}{\sigma/\sqrt{n}}\right) = 1 - Q\left(1.96 - \frac{\mu - 10}{0.1/\sqrt{10}}\right) - Q\left(c + \frac{\mu - 10}{0.1/\sqrt{10}}\right)$$

$$= 1 - Q(101.96 - 10\mu) - Q(98.04 + 10\mu)$$

It is plotted on the following page.

Problem 7-5

(a) The sample mean is $\bar{x} = 60.135$. At a 5% significance level the critical region is bounded by (-1.96, 1.96) (see Problem 7-4). We compute

$$Y = \frac{\bar{x} - \mu_0}{\sigma/\sqrt{n}} = \frac{60.135 - 60}{\sqrt{0.64}/\sqrt{10}} = 0.534$$

Since $-1.96 \le Y \le 1.96$), we accept the hypothesis that the bar is 60 oz. The OC curve is found from

$$\beta(\mu) = 1 - Q\left(c - \frac{\mu - \mu_0}{\sigma/\sqrt{n}}\right) - Q\left(c + \frac{\mu - \mu_0}{\sigma/\sqrt{n}}\right)$$

$$= 1 - Q\left(1.96 - \frac{\mu - 60}{0.64/\sqrt{10}}\right) - Q\left(c + \frac{\mu - 60}{0.64/\sqrt{10}}\right)$$

$$= 1 - Q(239.31 - 3.953\mu) - Q(235.211 + 3.953\mu)$$

The OC curve is shown below.
OC curve for Problem 7.4:

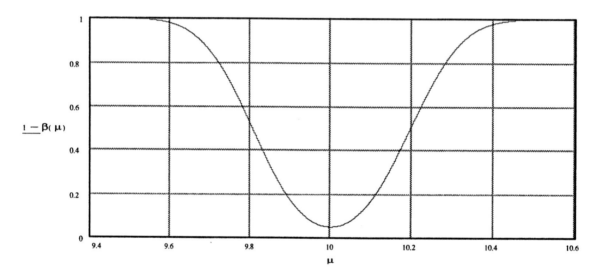

OC curve for Problem 7.5:

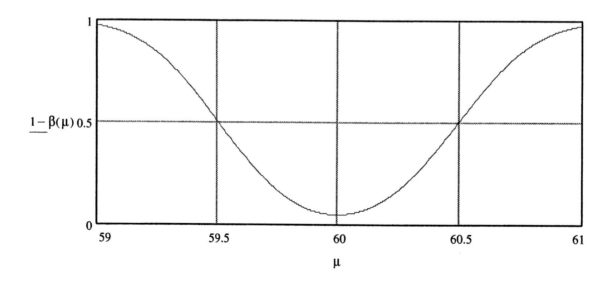

Problem 7-6

The hypotheses are

$$H_0: \mu = \mu_0 = 60 \text{ oz}$$

$$H_1: \mu < 60 \text{ oz}$$

or

$$H_0: \mu = \mu_0 = 60 \text{ oz}$$

$$H_1: \mu > 60 \text{ oz}$$

With the former test, we note that a positive value for the test statistic

$$Z = \frac{\bar{x} - \mu_0}{\sigma/\sqrt{n}}$$

would not lead to the conclusion that $\mu = \mu_0$ is false. Thus we reject H_0 only if $Z < -c$ where c is found from (7-37). At a 2% significance level, c is found to be 2.326. In Problem 7-5, Z was found to be 0.534. Since this is outside the range $(-2.326, 0]$, we reject the hypothesis that the bar is 60 oz. (Note that if we had used the second hypothesis test, we would have accepted the hypothesis.) From (7-48) we find the OC curve to be given by

$$\beta(\mu) = 0.5 - Q\left(c + \frac{\mu - \mu_0}{\sigma/\sqrt{n}}\right) = 0.5 - Q\left(2.326 + \frac{\mu - 60}{\sqrt{0.64}/\sqrt{10}}\right)$$

Problem 7-7

From a table of Q-functions or a rational approximation and trial and error, we find that $Q(T/\sigma) = 0.001$ has the solution $T/\sigma = 3.09$. A plot of the probability of detection is shown to the right:

$P_D(A\_\sigma)$

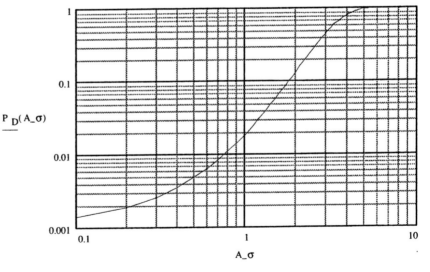

Problem 7-8

The test is to choose that number, n, such that

$$p(Z \mid H_n) = \frac{1}{2} e^{-|Z-n|} = \text{maximum for } n = 1, 2, 3, 4, 5, 6$$

or that

$$|Z - n| = \text{minimum}, \quad n = 1, 2, 3, 4, 5, 6$$

With $Z = 5.2$, the choice is clearly $n = 5$. The probability of making a correct decision on a given number m, say, is the probability that the noise is greater than -1/2 or less than 1/2. If not, another number will be chosen. This probability is

$$P_{\text{correct}} = \int_{-0.5}^{0.5} \frac{1}{2} e^{-|\alpha|} d\alpha = \int_{0}^{0.5} e^{-\alpha} d\alpha = -e^{-\alpha} \Big|_{0}^{0.5} = 1 - e^{-0.5}$$

Given a particular number m, the probability of making an error is

$$P_e = 1 - (1 - e^{-0.5}) = e^{-0.5} = 0.605$$

Since it is independent of the number chosen, this the average probability of making an error over all possible numbers $1, 2, \ldots, 6$.

CHAPTER 8
RELIABILITY

Problem 8-1

By definition

$$E(T) = \int_0^\infty t f(t)\, dt$$

But

$$f(t) = \frac{dF(t)}{dt} = \frac{d}{dt}[1 - R(t)] = -\frac{dR(t)}{dt}$$

So

$$E(T) = -\int_0^\infty t \frac{dR(t)}{dt}\, dt$$

Integrate by parts

$$E(T) = -tR(t)\Big|_0^\infty + \int_0^\infty R(t)\, dt = \int_0^\infty R(t)\, dt$$

where $R(\infty) = 0$ makes the term in front of the integral 0.

Problem 8-2

By definition

$$P(T \geq t) = R(t) = e^{-\lambda t},\ t \geq 0$$

We want $P(T \geq 5 \text{ years}) = 0.5$ or

$$e^{-\lambda(5 \text{ years})} = 0.5 \text{ or } \lambda = -\frac{\ln(0.5)}{5 \text{ years}} = 0.1386 \text{ yr}^{-1}$$

Problem 8-3

(a) From (8-2)

$$R(t) = e^{-\int_0^t 0.1 \, d\lambda} = e^{-0.1t}, \; t \geq 0$$

where t is in years.

(b) The mean time to failure is

$$\text{MTTF} = \int_0^\infty R(t) \, dt = \int_0^\infty e^{-0.1t} \, dt = -10 e^{-0.1t} \Big|_0^\infty = 10 \text{ years}$$

Problem 8-4

From (8-21)

$$R(t) = e^{-\int_0^t K \, d\lambda} = e^{-Kt}$$

We need K in hours^{-1}:

$$K = 2 \text{ PPM/K} = \frac{2}{10^6 \times 10^3 \text{ hours}} = 2 \times 10^{-9} \text{ hour}^{-1}$$

The mean time to failure is

$$\text{MTTF} = \int_0^\infty R(t) \, dt = \int_0^\infty e^{-Kt} \, dt$$

$$= -\frac{1}{K} e^{-Kt} \Big|_0^\infty = \frac{1}{K}$$

$$= 5 \times 10^8 \text{ hours}$$

$$= \frac{5 \times 10^8}{(365)(24)} = 5.7 \times 10^4 \text{ years}$$

88

Problem 8-5

```
%       MATLAB solution for Pr 8_5
%
male_stat = [100000 81049 76601 74645 73378 72430 70315 68827 ...
        66790 63989 61021 57767 54137 49982 45385 39986];
age = [1 2 3 4 5 10 15 20 25 30 35 40 45 50 55];
male_stat_shift(1:15) = male_stat(2:16);
male_stat_trunc(1:15) = male_stat(1:15);
male_fail_rate = (male_stat_trunc - male_stat_shift)./male_stat_shift;
female_stat = [100000 83807 79276 77246 75933 74940 72654 70924 ...
        68678 65932 62965 59759 56389 52906 49249 44787];
female_stat_shift(1:15) = female_stat(2:16);
female_stat_trunc(1:15) = female_stat(1:15);
female_fail_rate = (female_stat_trunc - female_stat_shift)./female_stat_shift;
subplot(2,1,1),plot(age,male_fail_rate),axis([0 60 0 0.25]), ...
        ylabel('failure rate, failures/yr'), grid, title('Failure rate for U.S. males')
subplot(2,1,2),plot(age,female_fail_rate),axis([0 60 0 0.25]), xlabel('age, years'),...
        ylabel('failure rate, failures/yr'), grid, title('Failure rate for U.S. females')
```

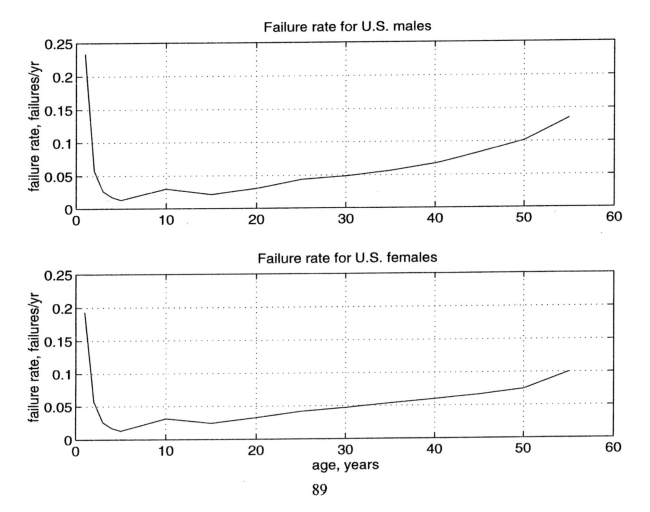

Problem 8-6

(a) The cdf for the failure time is

$$F(t) = \int_{-\infty}^{t} f(\lambda) d\lambda = \begin{cases} 0, & t < 0 \\ \int_{0}^{t} \dfrac{2\lambda}{T^2} d\lambda, & 0 \le t \le T \\ 1, & t > T \end{cases}$$

$$= \begin{cases} 0, & t < 0 \\ \left(\dfrac{t}{T}\right)^2, & 0 \le t \le T \\ 1, & t > T \end{cases}$$

The reliability function is

$$R(t) = 1 - F(t) = \begin{cases} 1 - \left(\dfrac{t}{T}\right)^2, & 0 \le t \le T \\ 0, & t > T \end{cases}$$

The failure rate function is

$$h(t) = \frac{f(t)}{R(t)} = \begin{cases} \dfrac{2t}{T^2 - t^2}, & 0 \le t \le T \\ 0, & \text{otherwise} \end{cases}$$

(b) The mean time to failure is

$$\text{MTTF} = \int_{0}^{\infty} R(t) dt = \int_{0}^{T} \left(1 - \frac{t^2}{T^2}\right) dt = \left[t - \frac{t^3}{3T^2}\right]_{0}^{T} = \frac{2}{3}T$$

90

Problem 8-7

(a) The system reliability is

$$R = P[(T_1 > t) \cap (T_2 > t) \cup (T_3 > t)]$$

$$= 1 - P[(T_1 > t) \cap (T_2 > t)] P(T_3 \le t)$$

$$= 1 - P(T_1 > t) P(T_2 > t)[1 - P(T_3 < t)]$$

$$= 1 - R_1 R_2 (1 - R_3) = 1 - r^2 f$$

(b) For this system

$$R = P[(T_1 > t) \cup (T_2 > t) \cap (T_3 > t)]$$

$$= P[(T_1 > t) \cup (T_2 > t)] P(T_3 > t)$$

$$= 1 - P[(T_1 \le t) \cap (T_2 \le t)] P(T_3 > t)]$$

$$= 1 - (1 - R_1)(1 - R_2) R_3 = 1 - (1 - r^2) r = 1 - f^2 r$$

(c) For a series system

$$R = P[(T_1 > t) \cap (T_2 > t) \cap (T_3 > t)] = \prod_{i=1}^{3} P(T_i > t) = r^3$$

(d) For this system

$$R = P\{[(T_1 > t) \cup (T_2 > t)] \cap [(T_3 > t) \cup (T_4 > t)]\}$$

$$= P[(T_1 > t) \cup (T_2 > t)] P[(T_3 > t) \cup (T_4 > t)]$$

$$= \{1 - P[(T_1 \le t) \cup (T_2 \le t)]\}\{1 - P[(T_3 \le t) \cup (T_4 \le t)]\}$$

$$= [1 - f_1 f_2][1 - f_3 f_4] = [1 - f^2]^2$$

(e) The reliability of this system can be deduced from the answer to part (d). We now have three systems in parallel in series with two systems in series. Thus

$$R = [1 - f_1 f_2 f_3][1 - f_4 f_5] = [1 - f^3][1 - f^2]$$

91

Plots of the system reliability versus the component reliability are given below for all systems.

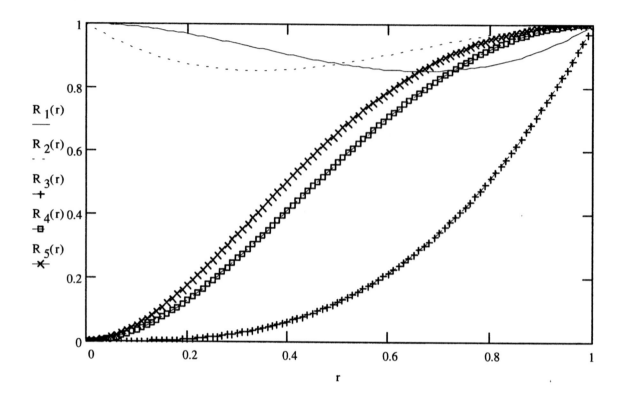

Problem 8-8

The overall system reliability for the computer system is

$$R = 1 - (1 - r)^3$$

where r is the reliability of each computer. Therefore solve

$$1 - (1 - r)^3 = 0.999 \text{ or } r = 0.9$$

Problem 8-9

Generalize the result for Problem 8-8 to n parallel components:

$$R = 1 - (1 - r)^n$$

Now let $R = 0.999$ and $r = 0.95$. Solve for n:

$$1 - (1 - 0.95)^n = 0.999 \text{ or } (0.05)^n = 0.001 \text{ or } n = \frac{\ln(0.001)}{\ln(0.05)} = 2.306$$

Round up to 3 parallel components to give an overall reliability of at least 0.999.

Problem 8-10

For an exponential failure pdf:

$$\text{MTTF} = \frac{1}{\lambda} = 100 \text{ days}$$

so $\lambda = 0.01$ days^{-1}. For a one system in standby to the system in service, the failure pdf is

$$f_{sb}(t) = \int_{-\infty}^{\infty} f_1(t - \eta) f_2(\eta) d\eta$$

$$= \int_0^t \lambda e^{-\lambda(t - \eta)} \lambda e^{-\lambda\eta} d\eta$$

$$= \lambda^2 t e^{-\lambda t} = 10^{-4} t e^{-10^{-2}t}, \ t \geq 0$$

which is (8-50). For a standby system

$$\text{MTTF} = \text{MTTF}_1 + \text{MTTF}_2 = 100 + 100 = 200 \text{ days}$$

Problem 8-11

For series systems

$$R_s(t) = \prod_{i=1}^{n} R_i(t) = \prod_{i=1}^{20} R_i(t) \prod_{j=1}^{300} R_j(t) \prod_{i=1}^{10} R_k(t) = R_{IC}^{20}(t) R_R^{300}(t) R_D^{10}(t)$$

But

$$R_{component}(t) = e^{-\lambda_{component} t}$$

so

93

$$R_x(t) = e^{-20\lambda_{IC}t} e^{-300\lambda_R t} e^{-10\lambda_D t}$$

Converting from failures in time to failures per hour, we have

$$\lambda_{IC} = 5 \text{ FIT} = \frac{5}{10^6 \times 10^3} = 5 \times 10^{-9} \text{ failures/hour}$$

$$\lambda_R = 20 \text{ FIT} = \frac{20}{10^6 \times 10^3} = 20 \times 10^{-9} \text{ failures/hour}$$

$$\lambda_D = 10 \text{ FIT} = \frac{10}{10^6 \times 10^3} = 10 \times 10^{-9} \text{ failures/hour}$$

For 5000 hours

$$R_x(5000) = e^{-20 \times 5 \times 10^{-9} \times 5000} e^{-20 \times 20 \times 10^{-9} \times 5000} e^{-20 \times 10 \times 10^{-9} \times 5000}$$

$$= e^{-5 \times 10^{-4}} e^{-0.03} e^{-5 \times 10^{-4}}$$

$$= (0.9995)^2 (0.9704) = 0.9695$$

Problem 8-12

(a) For the Weibull distribution

$$F(t) = 1 - e^{-(t/c)^m}, \ t \geq 0$$

which is (8-57). The reliability function is

$$R(t) = e^{-(t/c)^m} = e^{-(t/10)^2}$$

for $m = 2$ and $t = 10$ seconds.
(b) The mean time to failure is

$$\text{MTTF} = \int_0^\infty R(t)\,dt = \int_0^\infty e^{-t^2/100}\,dt = \int_0^\infty e^{-0.01t^2}\,dt = \frac{1}{2}\sqrt{\frac{\pi}{0.01}} = 8.862 \text{ seconds}$$

CHAPTER 9
INTRODUCTION TO RANDOM PROCESSES

Problem 9-1

(a) We get the following frequencies for each sample function:

$$X(t, \zeta) = 3 \quad \text{frequency one-half}$$

$$X(t, \zeta) = 2 \quad \text{frequency one-sixth}$$

$$X(t, \zeta) = 1 \quad \text{frequency one-third}$$

The sample functions are horizontal lines at each of these levels with the corresponding frequencies of occurrence.

(b) Now the sample functions and their frequencies of occurrence are

$$X(t, \zeta) = 2t \quad \text{frequency one-third}$$

$$X(t, \zeta) = -2t \quad \text{frequency one-third}$$

$$X(t, \zeta) = 0 \quad \text{frequency one-third}$$

Thus, one-third of the sample functions are lines with slope 1 going through the origin, one-third of them are lines with slope -1 going through the origin, and one-third of them are horizontal lines at level 0.

Problem 9-2

(a) Case 3: continuous independent variable and discrete dependent variable; (b) case 4: continuous independent variable and continuous dependent variable.

Problem 9-3

(a) Three computer-generated sample functions are shown below:

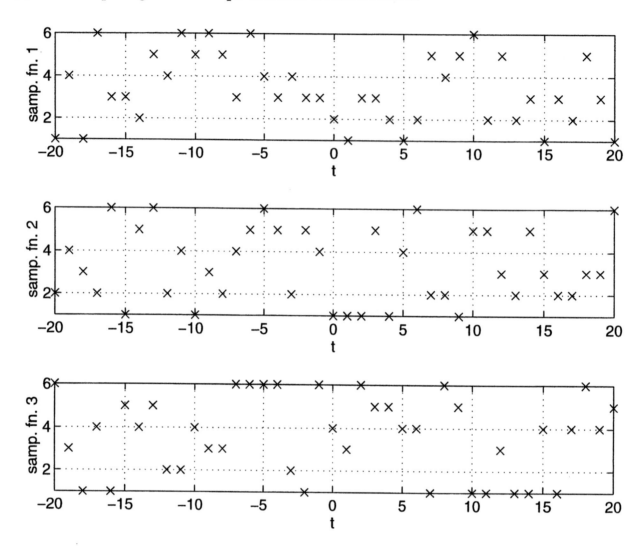

(b) Case 1: Discrete independent variable; discrete dependent variable.

Problem 9-4

(a) The ensemble-average mean is

$$E[X(t, \Theta)] = A \int_0^{\pi/4} \frac{4}{\pi} \cos(\omega_0 t + \theta) \, d\theta$$

$$= \frac{4A}{\pi} \sin(\omega_0 + t) \Big|_0^{\pi/4}$$

$$= \frac{4A}{\pi} [\sin(\omega_0 t + \pi/4) - \sin(\omega_0 t)]$$

The ensemble-average mean-square value is

$$E[X^2(t, \Theta)] = A^2 \int_0^{\pi/4} \frac{4}{\pi} \cos^2(\omega_0 t + \theta) \, d\theta$$

$$= \frac{4A^2}{\pi} \int_0^{\pi/4} \left[\frac{1}{2} + \frac{1}{2} \cos 2(\omega_0 t + \theta) \right] d\theta$$

$$= \frac{4A^2}{\pi} \left[\frac{\theta}{2} + \frac{1}{4} \sin 2(\omega_0 t + \theta) \right]_0^{\pi/4}$$

$$= \frac{A^2}{\pi} \left[\frac{\pi}{2} - 1 + \cos(2\omega_0 t) \right]$$

(b) The time-average mean of a single sample function is 0 and the time-average mean-square value of a single sample function is $A^2/2$.

(c) It is neither stationary nor ergodic.

Problem 9-5

The ensemble-average autocorrelation function is

$$R(t, t + \tau) = \frac{4A^2}{\pi} \int_0^{\pi/4} \sin(\omega_0 t + \theta) \sin[\omega_0(t + \tau) + \theta] \, d\theta$$

$$= \frac{2A^2}{\pi} \int_0^{\pi/4} [\cos(\omega_0 t) - \cos(2\omega_0 t + 2\omega_0 \tau + 2\theta)] \, d\theta$$

$$= \frac{2A^2}{\pi} \left[(\cos \omega_0 \tau) \theta - \frac{1}{2} \sin(2\omega_0 t + 2\omega_0 \tau + 2\theta) \right]_0^{\pi/4}$$

$$= \frac{2A^2}{\pi} \left[(\cos \omega_0 \tau) \frac{\pi}{4} - \frac{1}{2} \sin(2\omega_0 t + 2\omega_0 \tau + \pi/2) + \frac{1}{2} \sin(2\omega_0 t + 2\omega_0 \tau) \right]$$

$$= \frac{2A^2}{\pi} \left[(\cos \omega_0 \tau) \frac{\pi}{4} - \frac{1}{2} \cos[2\omega_0(t + \tau)] + \frac{1}{2} \sin[2\omega_0(t + \tau)] \right]$$

$$= \frac{2A^2}{\pi} \left[(\cos \omega_0 \tau) \frac{\pi}{4} + \frac{1}{\sqrt{2}} \cos[2\omega_0(t + \tau) + \pi/4] \right]$$

Problem 9-6

(a)

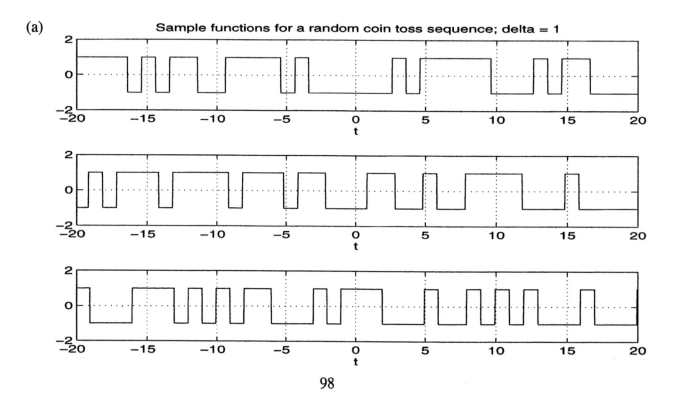

Sample functions for a random coin toss sequence; delta = 1

98

(b) Consider the interval $[0, \Delta]$. The autocorrelation function is, by definition,

$$R_X(\tau) = E[X(t)X(t + \tau)]$$

At an arbitrary time in this interval, we have two equiprobable possibilities with regard to the product $X(t)X(t + \tau)$: it can be A^2 or $-A^2$. If the sign of $X(t)$ changes in the interval $[0, \Delta]$, the probability of a sign match is $(1 - \tau/\Delta)$ (sketch this case to convince yourself) and the probability of a sign mismatch is τ/Δ, assuming $\tau > 0$. If the sign of $X(t)$ doesn't change in the interval, then the product $X(t)X(t + \tau) = A^2$, and this case happens with probability $1/2$. Thus the autocorrelation function in $[0, \Delta]$ is

$$R_X(\tau) = \frac{A^2}{2}\left[(-1)(-1)\left(1 - \frac{\tau}{\Delta}\right) + (1)(-1)\frac{\tau}{\Delta}\right] + \frac{1}{2}(A)(A) = A^2\left(1 - \frac{\tau}{\Delta}\right), \quad 0 \le \tau \le \Delta$$

A similar argument for $\tau > \Delta$ shows that the autocorrelation function is 0. By eveness of the autocorrelation function,

$$R_X(\tau) = \begin{cases} A^2(1 - |\tau|/\Delta), & 0 \le |\tau| \le \Delta \\ \\ 0, & \text{otherwise} \end{cases}$$

(c) The average power is A^2, or $R_X(0)$.

Problem 9-7

(a) Suitable; (b) not suitable - the function is not even and its maximum is not at zero; (c) Not suitable - its Fourier transform is not nonnegative.

Problem 9-8

(a) The mean-square value is $E[X^2(t)] = R_X(0) = A^2$; (b) its mean is $\lim_{\tau \to \infty} = 0$; (c) no, it is not a periodic process since its autocorrelation function is not periodic.

Problem 9-9

First, we need its mean and variance. We can get these from $E[X^2(t)] = R_X(0) = 2$ and $\text{mean}^2 = \lim_{\tau \to \infty} R_X(\tau) = 1$. Thus the variance of this process is $\sigma^2 = E(X^2) - E^2(X) = 2 - 1^2 = 1$. Hence its pdf is

$$f_X(x) = \frac{e^{-(x - \mu_X)^2/2\sigma_X^2}}{\sqrt{2\pi\sigma_X^2}} = \frac{e^{-(x - 1)^2/2}}{\sqrt{2\pi}}$$

Problem 9-10

Property 1 is shown as follows:

$$R_{XY}(\tau) = E[X(t)Y(t + \tau)]$$

$$R_{YX}(\tau) = E[Y(t)X(t + \tau)]$$

$$= E[X(t')Y(t' - \tau)], \quad t' = t + \tau$$

$$= R_{XY}(-\tau), \quad \text{by wide sense stationarity}$$

For Property 2, consider

$$E\{[aX(t) + Y(t + \tau)]^2\} = a^2 E[X^2(t)] + 2aE[X(t)Y(t + \tau)] + E[Y^2(t)]$$

$$= a^2 R_X(0) + 2a R_{XY}(\tau) + R_Y(0)$$

where stationarity of $\{X(t)\}$ and $\{Y(t)\}$ has been use. Since the left-hand side is the expectation of a squared quantity, it is clearly nonnegative. Hence the discriminant of the equivalent quadratic in a is negative, or

$$R_{XY}(\tau) - E[X^2(0)]E[Y^2(0)] \leq 0$$

Rearranging this expression produces the desired property. Finally, for Property 3, consider

$$E\{[X(t) \pm Y(t + \tau)]\} \geq 0$$

$$\text{or } E[X^2(t)] \pm 2E[X(t)Y(t + \tau)] + E[Y^2(t + \tau)] \geq 0$$

$$\text{or } R_X(0) \pm 2R_{XY}(\tau) + R_Y(0) \geq 0$$

When the two inequalities are rearranged, the stated property follows.

Problem 9-11

(a) Their average powers are

$$P_X = R_X(0) = 1 \text{ and } P_Y = R_Y(0) = 1$$

(b) The autocorrelation function of their sum is

$$R_Z(\tau) = R_X(\tau) + R_{XY}(\tau) + R_{YX}(-\tau) + R_Y(\tau)$$

$$= \cos(2\pi f_0 \tau) + \sin(3\pi f_0 \tau + \pi/3) + \sin[3\pi f_0(-\tau) + \pi/3] + \cos(4\pi f_0 \tau)$$

$$= \cos(2\pi f_0 \tau) + \cos(4\pi f_0 \tau) + 2\sin(\pi/3)\cos(3\pi f_0 \tau)$$

(c) The average power of their sum is

$$E(Z^2) = R_Z(0) = 1 + 1 + 2\sin(\pi/3) = 3.732$$

Problem 9-12

The derivation follows:

$$C_{XY} = E\{[X(t) - \overline{X(t)}][Y(t) - \overline{Y(t)}]\}$$

$$= E[X(t)Y(t) - \overline{X(t)}Y(t) - \overline{Y(t)}X(t) + \overline{X(t)}\ \overline{Y(t)}]$$

$$= E[X(t)Y(t)] - \overline{X(t)}\ \overline{Y(t)} - \overline{Y(t)}\ \overline{X(t)} + \overline{X(t)}\ \overline{Y(t)}$$

$$= E[X(t)Y(t)] - \overline{X(t)}\ \overline{Y(t)}$$

Problem 9-13

(a) From the covariance function $r(1 \text{ second}) = 0.5$. Since $r(\infty) = 0$, the mean is zero. Thus the variance is equal to the mean-square value which is equal to the power or 4 watts. From (9-42) it follows that

$$f_{X_1 X_2}(x_1, x_2, \tau = 1 \text{ sec}) = \frac{e^{-\frac{x_1^2 - 2(0.5)x_1 x_2 + x_2^2}{2(4)(1 - 0.25)}}}{2\pi(4)\sqrt{1 - 0.25}} = \frac{e^{-\frac{1}{6}(x_1^2 - x_1 x_2 + x_2^2)}}{6.92\pi}$$

(b) At $\tau = 3$ sec, $r(3) = 0$, so the samples at 3 seconds separation are uncorrelated. Hence

101

$$f_{X_1 X_2}(x_1, x_2, \tau = 3 \text{ sec}) = \frac{e^{-x_1^2/8}}{\sqrt{8\pi}} \frac{e^{-x_2^2/8}}{\sqrt{8\pi}} = \frac{e^{-(x_1^2 + x_2^2)/8}}{8\pi}$$

Problem 9-14

The variance is

$$\sigma_Z^2 = \int_0^T \int_0^T \sigma^2 r(\zeta - t) \, dt \, d\tau$$

Make the transformation of variables $u = \zeta - t$ and $v = \zeta$. The area of integration transforms from a square of side T to a trapezoid as shown below:

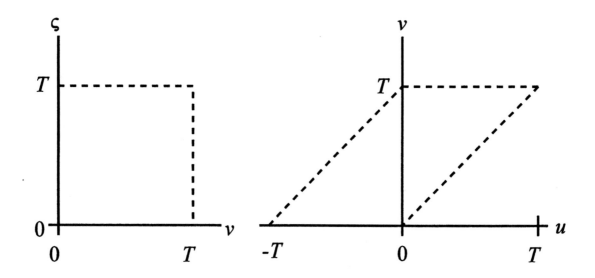

We now integrate over the trapezoidal area shown on the right to get the variance of Z:

$$\sigma_Z^2 = \int\limits_{u=-T}^{0} \int\limits_{v=0}^{u+T} \sigma^2 r(u)\,dv\,du + \int\limits_{u=0}^{T} \int\limits_{v=u}^{T} \sigma^2 r(u)\,dv\,du$$

$$= \sigma^2 \left[\int\limits_{u=-T}^{0} (u+T)\,r(u)\,du + \int\limits_{0}^{T} (T-u)\,r(u)\,du \right]$$

$$= \sigma^2 \int\limits_{-T}^{T} (T - |u|)(1 - |u|/2)\,du$$

$$= \sigma^2 T \int\limits_{-T}^{T} (1 - |u|/T)\,r(u)\,du$$

The integrand is even, so we can double the integral and integrate from 0 to T.

$$\sigma_Z^2 = \begin{cases} 2\sigma^2 T \int\limits_{0}^{2} (1 - u/T)(1 - u/2)\,du, & T > 2 \\[2ex] 2\sigma^2 T \int\limits_{0}^{T} (1 - u/T)(1 - u/2)\,du, & T \le 2 \end{cases}$$

When the integrals are carried out, the result is

$$\sigma_Z^2 = \begin{cases} \sigma^2 T(T - T^2/6), & T > 2 \\[2ex] \sigma^2 T(2 - 4/3T), & T \le 2 \end{cases}$$

Recalling that $\sigma_Z{}^2 = N_0/2$, we find the probability of error to be

$$P_E = \begin{cases} Q\left(\sqrt{\dfrac{2A^2 T}{N_0(T - T^2/6)}} \right), & T > 2 \\[3ex] Q\left(\sqrt{\dfrac{2A^2 T}{N_0(2 - 4/3T)}} \right), & T \le 2 \end{cases}$$

A plot is given on the next page for $T = 1$, 2, and 10 seconds.

103

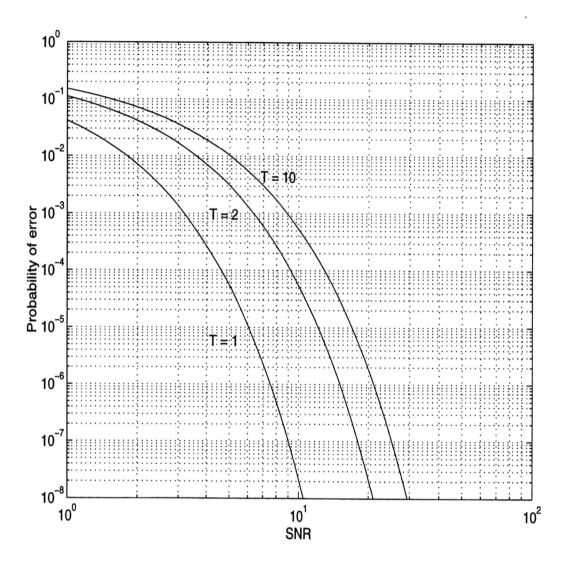

Problem 9-15

By definition of a conditional pdf:

$$f(x \mid y) = \frac{f_{XY}(x, y)}{f_Y(y)} = \frac{e^{-\frac{x^2 - 2rxy + y^2}{2\sigma^2(1 - r^2)}}}{2\pi\sigma^2\sqrt{1 - r^2}} \frac{\sqrt{2\pi\sigma^2}}{e^{-y^2/2\sigma^2}} = \frac{e^{-\frac{x^2 - 2rxy + y^2}{2\sigma^2(1 - r^2)} + \frac{y^2}{2\sigma^2}}}{\sqrt{2\pi\sigma^2(1 - r^2)}}$$

Simplify the exponent:

104

$$-\frac{x^2 - 2rxy + y^2}{2\sigma^2(1 - r^2)} + \frac{y^2}{2\sigma^2} = -\frac{x^2}{2\sigma^2(1 - r^2)} - \frac{rxy}{\sigma^2(1 - r^2)} + \frac{y^2}{2\sigma^2(1 - r^2)} + \frac{y^2}{2\sigma^2}$$

$$= -\frac{x^2 - rxy + r^2y^2}{2\sigma^2(1 - r^2)} = -\frac{(x - ry)^2}{2\sigma^2(1 - r^2)}$$

Thus, the conditional pdf is

$$f(x \mid y) = \frac{e^{-\frac{(x - ry)^2}{2\sigma^2(1 - r^2)}}}{\sqrt{2\pi\sigma^2(1 - r^2)}}$$

Problem 9-16

From (9-61):

$$R_X(0) = \alpha^{|0|}\frac{1 - \alpha}{1 + \alpha}\sigma_n^2$$

so

$$r_X(M) = \frac{R_X(M)}{R_X(0)} = \alpha^{|M|}$$

We want

$$\frac{\alpha^{|M + 1|}}{\alpha^{|M|}} \leq 0.6$$

Take the case $M \geq 0$ (the expression is even):

$$\alpha^{M + 1 - M} \leq 0.6 \text{ or } \alpha = 0.6$$

Thus

$$r_X(M) = 0.6^{|M|} = \{\cdots, 0.36, 0.6, 1, 0.6, 0.36, \cdots\}$$

Problem 9-17

From (9-61) and (9-63):

$$r_X(M) = \frac{R_X(M)}{R_X(0)} = \alpha^{|M|} = 0.3^{|M|}$$

The correlation coefficient for adjacent sample values is

$$r_X(1) = 0.3$$

Thus, the joint pdf of adjacent samples is

$$f(x_1, x_2; 1) = \frac{e^{-\frac{x_1^2 - 2(0.3)x_1x_2 + x_2^2}{2(1)(1 - 0.9)}}}{2\pi\sqrt{1 - 0.09}} = \frac{e^{-\frac{x_1^2 - 0.6x_1x_2 + x_2^2}{0.2}}}{2\pi\sqrt{0.91}}$$

CHAPTER 10
RANDOM PROCESSES THROUGH SYSTEMS

Problem 10-1

Probability of dc component = 1 - 2Q(c/σ). Probability of ac component = 1 - Probability of dc component. Therefore

$$1 - [1 - 2Q(c/\sigma)] = 1 - 2Q(c/\sigma) \quad \text{or} \quad Q(c/\sigma) = 0.25$$

From Table C-2, Q(0.7) = 0.242 $\approx$ 0.25. Hence $c/\sigma = 0.7$ is close.

Problem 10-2

A MATLAB program that generates sample functions of the limiter output is given below. The input is a first-order autoregressive process generated according to (9-54). Note that the limited sample functions should be either 1 or -1. The slanted lines come about because of the plotting routine.

```
%       Solution for Problem 10-2; a 1st order autoregressive process is used to drive the limiter
%
alpha = input('Enter value for alpha (see eq. 9-54)  (< 1) ');
sigma2 = input('Enter variance of driving random process ');
a = input('Enter limiter amplitude ');
N = input('Enter total number of Gaussian random variables to generate ');
sigma_X = sqrt(sigma2)*sqrt((1 - alpha)/(1 + alpha));
beta = 1 - alpha;
NN=sqrt(sigma2)*randn(1,N);
X = zeros(size(NN));
X(1) = 0;
t = zeros(size(NN));
for k = 2:N
        X(k) = alpha*X(k-1) + beta*NN(k);
        t(k) = (k-1);
end
Y = a*sign(X);
subplot(211),plot(t,X,'-w'),axis([400 500 -3*sigma_X 3*sigma_X]),...
        grid,xlabel('t'),ylabel('limiter input ampli'),...
        title(['limiter output (bottom) for autoregressive input with alpha = ',num2str(alpha)])
subplot(212),plot(t,Y,'-w'),axis([400 500 -2*a 2*a]),grid,...
        xlabel('t'),ylabel('limiter output ampli')
```

Input and output sample functions are shown below for $\alpha = 0.1$ and $\alpha = 0.9$.

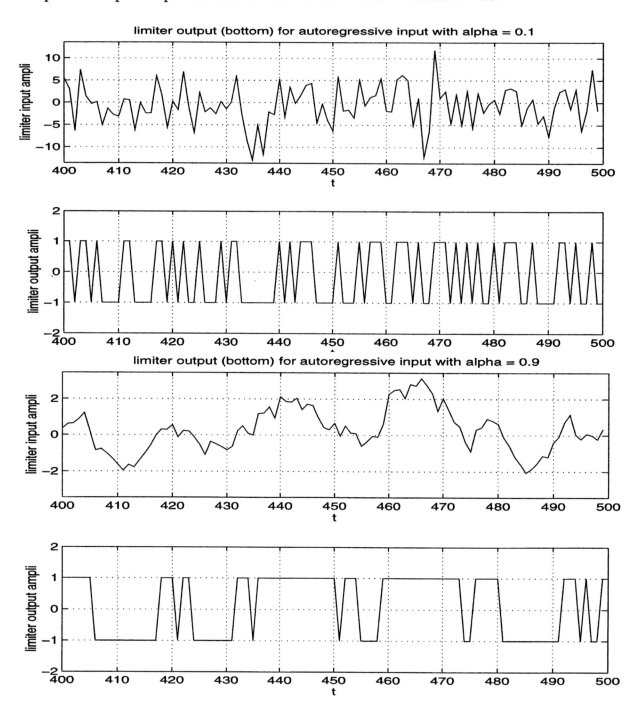

By stationarity and symmetry of the input waveform about the t-axis,

$$f_Y(y; t) = 0.5\delta(y - a) + 0.5\delta(y - a)$$

108

Problem 10-3

From (10-16):

$$\text{Power in dc component} = \frac{A^4}{4} + 2R_s(0)R_n(0) + R_n^2(0)$$

and

$$\text{Power in components at } \pm 2f_0 = \frac{A^4}{16} + \frac{A^4}{16} = \frac{A^4}{8}$$

But, the autocorrelation function of the input signal is, from the inverse Fourier transform of (9-26),

$$R_s(\tau) = \frac{A^2}{2}\cos(\omega_0\tau)$$

so $R_s(0) = A^2/2$. Also, let $R_n(0) = P_n$, so the condition for the power in the dc component at the output equal to four times the power in the sinusoidal component is

$$\frac{A^4}{4} + 2\frac{A^2}{2}P_n + P_n^2 = 4\frac{A^4}{8}$$

or

$$P_n^2 + A^2 P_n - \frac{A^4}{4} = 0$$

which, when solved for the positive solution, gives

$$P_n = \frac{-A^2 + \sqrt{2}A^2}{2} = 0.207A^2$$

Problem 10-4

(a) The dc power is the integral of the delta function, or 25, which is also the mean squared. Thus $m_X = 5$; (b) $H(0) = 1$; (c) from (a) and (b), $m_Y = m_X = 5$; (d) the magnitude of the transfer function squared is

$$|H(f)|^2 = \frac{1}{1 + f^4/f_3^4}$$

so

$$S_Y(f) = |H(f)|^2 S_X(f) = 25\delta(f) + \frac{40}{(f^2 + 4)(f^4 + 4)}$$

(e) The cross-spectral density, from (10-27), is

$$S_{XY}(f) = S_X(f)H(f) = 25\delta(f) + \frac{20}{(f^2 + 4)(2 + j2f - f^2)}$$

Problem 10-5

In (10-34), let

$$A = \frac{N_0}{2(R_1C)^2} \quad \text{and} \quad \alpha = \frac{R_1 + R_2}{R_1 R_2 C}$$

Then

$$E[Y^2] = R_Y(0) = \int_{-\infty}^{\infty} S_Y(f) df = \int_{-\infty}^{\infty} \frac{A}{\alpha^2 + (2\pi f)^2} df$$

Because the integrand is even, we can double the integral and integrate from 0 to ∞:

$$E[Y^2] = 2\int_{0}^{\infty} \frac{A}{\alpha^2 + (2\pi f)^2} df = \frac{2A}{\alpha^2} \frac{\alpha}{2\pi} \int_{0}^{\infty} \frac{du}{1 + u^2} = \frac{2A}{\alpha^2} \frac{\alpha}{2\pi} \tan^{-1}(u) \Big|_{0}^{\infty}$$

$$= \frac{A}{2\alpha} = \frac{R_2 N_0}{4R_1 C(R_1 + R_2)}$$

Problem 10-6

(a) The autocorrelation function is

$$R_Y(\tau) = E[Y(t)Y(t + \tau)] = E\{[X(t) + X(t - T)][X(t) + X(t - T + \tau)]]\}$$

$$= E\{X(t)X(t + \tau) + X(t)X(t + \tau - T) + X(t - T)X(t + \tau) + X(t - T)X(t + \tau - T)\}$$

Take the expectation of each term separately and use the definition of the autocorrelation function, which is $R_X(\tau) = E[X(t)X(t + \tau)]$:

$$R_Y(\tau) = E[X(t)X(t + \tau)] + E[X(t)X(t + \tau - T)] + E[X(t - T)X(t + \tau)] + E[X(t - T)X(t + \tau - T)]$$

$$= R_X(\tau) + R_X(\tau - T) + R_X(\tau + T) + R_X(\tau) = 2R_X(\tau) + R_X(\tau - T) + R_X(\tau + T)$$

(b) The power spectral density is the Fourier transform of the autocorrelation function. Using appropriate transform theorems (see Appendix A), we get

$$S_Y(f) = \mathscr{F}[R_Y(\tau)] = 2\mathscr{F}[R_X(\tau)] + \mathscr{F}[R_X(\tau - T)] + \mathscr{F}[R_X(\tau + T)]$$

$$= 2S_X(f) + S_X(f)e^{-j2\pi fT} + S_X(f)e^{j2\pi fT} = 2S_X(f)[1 + \cos(2\pi fT)]$$

$$= 4S_X(f)\cos^2(\pi fT)$$

where appropriate trigonometric identies have been used to get the last two expressions.

Problem 10-7

(a) The transfer function is

$$H(f) = \mathscr{F}[Ae^{-\alpha t}u(t)] = \frac{A}{\alpha + j2\pi f}$$

The power spectral density of the output is

$$S_Y(f) = |H(f)|^2 S_X(f) = \frac{A^2}{\alpha^2 + (2\pi f)^2} \frac{B}{\beta^2 + (2\pi f)^2}$$

$$= \frac{K_1}{\alpha + j2\pi f} + \frac{K_1^*}{\alpha - j2\pi f} + \frac{K_2}{\beta + j2\pi f} + \frac{K_2^*}{\beta - j2\pi f}$$

Use Heaviside's expansion rule to find K_1:

$$K_1 = (\alpha + j2\pi f)S_Y(f)\big|_{j2\pi f = -\alpha} = \frac{A^2}{\alpha - j2\pi f}\frac{B}{\beta^2 + (2\pi f)^2}\Bigg|_{j2\pi f = -\alpha} = \frac{A^2}{2\alpha}\frac{B}{\beta^2 + \alpha^2}$$

Similarly,

$$K_2 = \frac{A^2}{\alpha^2 + \beta^2}\frac{B}{2\beta}$$

Put the terms in $S_Y(f)$ involving K_1 together and those involving K_2 together to get

$$S_Y(f) = \frac{A^2 B}{\alpha^2 + \beta^2}\frac{1}{\alpha^2 + (2\pi f)^2} + \frac{A^2 B}{\alpha^2 + \beta^2}\frac{1}{\beta^2 + (2\pi f)^2}$$

$$= \frac{A^2 B}{\alpha^2 + \beta^2}\left[\frac{1}{2\alpha}\frac{2\alpha}{\alpha^2 + (2\pi f)^2} + \frac{1}{2\alpha}\frac{2\alpha}{\alpha^2 + (2\pi f)^2}\right]$$

The inverse Fourier transform gives the autocorrelation function:

$$R_Y(\tau) = \frac{A^2 B}{\alpha^2 + \beta^2}\left[\frac{1}{2\alpha}e^{-\alpha|\tau|} + \frac{1}{2\beta}e^{-\beta|\tau|}\right]$$

(c) The cross-spectral density of input and output is

$$S_{XY}(f) = H(f)S_X(f) = \frac{A}{\alpha + j2\pi f}\frac{B}{\beta^2 + (2\pi f)^2}$$

(d) The cross-correlation function of input with output is

$$R_{XY}(\tau) = \mathscr{F}^{-1}\left[S_{XY}(f)\right]$$

Expand $S_{XY}(f)$ using partial fractions:

$$S_{XY}(f) = \frac{K_1}{\alpha + j2\pi f} + \frac{K_2}{\beta + j2\pi f} + \frac{K_2^*}{\beta - j2\pi f}$$

112

Use Heaviside's expansion rule to find

$$K_2 = \frac{AB}{(\alpha + j2\pi f)(\beta - j2\pi f)}\bigg|_{j2\pi f = -\beta} = \frac{AB}{(\alpha - \beta)(2\beta)}$$

Similarly, we find K_1 to be

$$K_1 = \frac{AB}{\beta^2 + \alpha^2}$$

Put the terms involving K_2 and K_2^* together to get

$$R_{XY}(\tau) = \mathscr{F}^{-1}[S_{XY}(f)]$$

$$= \mathscr{F}^{-1}\left[\frac{AB}{\beta^2 + \alpha^2} \frac{1}{\alpha + j2\pi f} + \frac{AB}{2\beta(\alpha - \beta)} \frac{2\beta}{\beta^2 + (2\pi f)^2}\right]$$

$$= \frac{AB}{\alpha^2 + \beta^2} e^{-\alpha\tau} u(\tau) + \frac{AB}{2\beta(\alpha - \beta)} e^{-\beta|\tau|}$$

Problem 10-8

The variance of $\{Y(t)\}$ at any time t, from (10-42), is

$$\sigma_Y^2 = \frac{R_2 N_0}{4(R_1 + R_2)R_1 C} = 45.5$$

The mean is zero. Thus, the first-order pdf of the output is

$$f_Y(y; t) = \frac{e^{-y^2/2(45.5)}}{\sqrt{2\pi(45.5)}} = \frac{e^{-y^2/91}}{\sqrt{91\pi}}$$

For the second-order pdf, we need the correlation coefficient. For times separated by 1 second, we find from (10-38) and (10-44) that

$$r = e^{-110} \approx 0$$

Thus, $\{Y(t)\}$ and $\{Y(t + 1\text{ s})\}$ are, for all practical purposes, independent since they are uncorrelated

Gaussian random variables, and

$$f_Y(y_1, y_2; t, t + 1s) = \frac{e^{-y_1^2/2(45.5)}}{\sqrt{2\pi(45.5)}} \frac{e^{-y_2^2/2(45.5)}}{\sqrt{2\pi(45.5)}} = \frac{e^{-(y_1^2 + y_2^2)/91}}{91\pi}$$

At a separation of $\tau = 0.1$ second, $r = e^{-110(0.1)} = e^{-11} \approx 0$, so the result is the same.

Problem 10-9

The autocorrelation function is the inverse Fourier transform of the power spectral density, so

$$R(\tau) = \mathscr{F}^{-1}\left\{ \begin{array}{l} \dfrac{N_0}{2}, \quad -B \le f \le B \\ \\ 0, \quad \text{otherwise} \end{array} \right\} = \int_{-B}^{B} \frac{N_0}{2} e^{j2\pi f\tau} df$$

$$= \frac{N_0}{2} \frac{e^{j2\pi f\tau}}{j2\pi\tau}\bigg|_{-B}^{B} = N_0 B \frac{\sin(2\pi B\tau)}{2\pi B\tau} = N_0 B\,\text{sinc}(2B\tau)$$

Note that the autocorrelation function is zero for integer multiples of $1/2B$ except for $\tau = 0$.

Problem 10-10

From (10-52):

$$h(\tau) = \frac{2}{N_0} R_{XY}(\tau) = \frac{2}{2} 5\pi e^{-10\pi\tau} u(\tau)$$

Use the Fourier transform pair (10-35) to get

$$H(f) = \frac{5\pi}{10\pi + j2\pi f} = \frac{0.5}{1 + j(f/5)}$$

Problem 10-11

Use the Fourier transform pair (10-35) to get

$$H(f) = \frac{5}{20 + j2\pi f}$$

This gives $H(0) = 0.25$. From (10-57):

$$B_N = \frac{1}{H^2(0)} \int_0^\infty |H(f)|^2 df = \frac{1}{0.25^2} \int_0^\infty \frac{25}{400 + (2\pi f)^2} df$$

$$= \frac{25}{40\pi(0.25)^2} \int_0^\infty \frac{du}{1 + u^2} = \frac{25}{40\pi(0.25)^2} \tan^{-1}(u) \Big|_0^\infty$$

$$= \frac{25}{40\pi(0.25)^2} \frac{\pi}{2} = 5 \text{ Hz}$$

Problem 10-12

(a) The magnitude squared of the transfer function is 16 for $-5 \le f \le 5$ and 4 for $-10 \le f \le -5$ and 5 $\le f \le 10$. Elsewhere it is zero. From (10-57) the noise equivalent bandwidth is

$$B_N = \frac{1}{16} \int_0^\infty |H|^2 df = \frac{1}{16}(16\times 5 + 4\times 5) = 6.25 \text{ Hz}$$

(b) $H(0) = 8$ and $H(f) = 8 - f$ for $0 \le f \le 8$, so

$$B_N = \frac{1}{64} \int_0^8 (8 - f)^2 df = -\frac{1}{64} \frac{(8 - f)^3}{3} \Big|_0^8 = 2.667 \text{ Hz}$$

Problem 10-13

(a) Use Nyquist's theorem. Looking back into the circuit, we see an equivalent resistance of 60,000 ohms. Thus

$$v_n^2 = 4kTR_{eq}B = 4(1.38 \times 10^{-23})(330)(60,000)(100,000) = 1.093 \times 10^{-10} \text{ volts}^2$$

or $v_n = 10.45$ micro volts rms.

(b) Now the equivalent resistance looking back into the circuit is 5,000 ohms in parallel with 1,000 ohms or 833.3 ohms. The mean-square noise voltage is

$$v_n^2 = 4kTR_{eq}B = 4(1.38 \times 10^{-23})(330)(833.3)(100,000) = 1.518 \times 10^{-12} \text{ volts}^2$$

or $v_n = 1.23$ micro volts rms.

Problem 10-14

Find the gains and noise figures as ratios:

Subsystem	G_k, ratio	F_k, ratio
1	31.62	1.78
2	0.32	3.16
3	100	2.51
4	1,000,000	5.01

From (10-63):

$$F_{overall} = 1.78 + \frac{3.16 - 1}{31.62} + \frac{2.51 - 1}{(31.62)(0.32)} + \frac{5.01 - 1}{(31.62)(0.32)(100)} = 2.0$$

In dB, $F_{overall} = 10 \log_{10} 2 = 3.01$ dB. The overall gain in dB is the sum of the overall gains in dB or $G_{overall} = 15 + (-5) + 20 + 60 = 90$ dB.

Problem 10-15

2.7 dB is 1.86 ratio. Thus, Friss' formula becomes

$$1.86 = 1.78 + \frac{3.16 - 1}{G_1} + \frac{2.51 - 1}{G_1(0.32)} + \frac{5.01 - 1}{G_1(0.32)(100)}$$

Solve for G_1 and get

$$G_1 = \frac{7}{0.08} = 87.55 \quad \text{or} \quad G_{1,\,dB} = 19.42 \text{ dB}$$

Problem 10-16

The spectra are shown below:

(a)

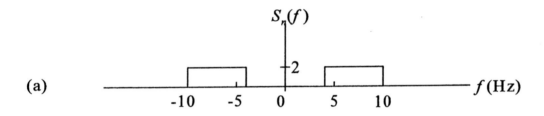

(b)

(c)

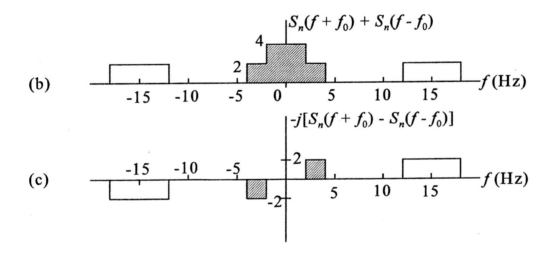

Problem 10-17

Specializing (10-83) to the assumptions of Example 10-16, we get

$$e_{min} = 2\int_0^\infty \frac{S_N(f)\,S_S(f)}{S_N(f) + S_S(f)}\,df$$

$$= N_0\int_0^\infty \frac{2B\alpha/(\alpha^2 + (2\pi f)^2)}{2B\alpha/(\alpha^2 + (2\pi f)^2) + N_0/2}\,df$$

$$= \frac{4B\alpha}{2\pi C}\int_0^\infty \frac{d(2\pi f)/C}{1 + (2\pi f/C)^2} = \frac{2B\alpha}{\pi C}\int_0^\infty \frac{du}{1 + u^2}$$

$$= \frac{2B\alpha}{\pi C}\,\tan^{-1}(u)\Big|_0^\infty$$

$$= \frac{2B\alpha}{\pi C}\,\frac{\pi}{2} = \frac{B}{\sqrt{\dfrac{4B}{N_0\alpha} + 1}}$$

where C has been defined as

$$C = \frac{4B\alpha}{N_0} + \alpha^2$$

and the substitution

$$u = \frac{2\pi f}{C}$$

has been used to simplify the integral.

118

```
%       Computer Exercise 1-1
%
N = input('Enter the number of random numbers to generate ');
M = input('Enter the number of histogram bins ');
X = rand(1,N);
Y = fix(10*X);
hist(Y,M),xlabel('independent variable'),...
        ylabel('number of occurrences'),...
        title(['histogram for ' num2str(N), ' trials'])
```

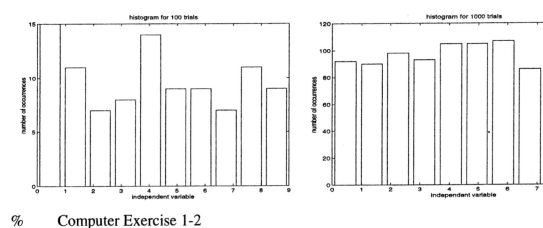

```
%       Computer Exercise 1-2
%
N = input('Enter the number of shims to simulate ');
M = input('Enter the number of histogram bins ');
T = input('Enter nominal thickness of shims in mm ');
tol = input('Enter +- tolerance around nominal thickness in mm ');
X = rand(1,N);
Y = (T - tol) + 2*tol*X;
hist(Y,M),xlabel('thickness in mm '),...
        ylabel('number of occurrences'),...
        title(['histogram for ' num2str(N), ' trials'])
```

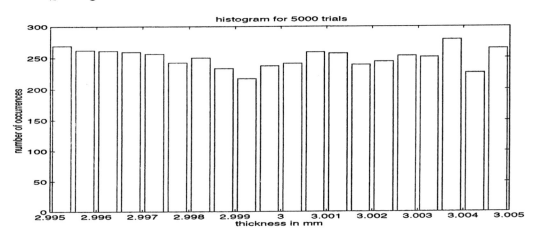

119

```
%       Computer Exercise 1-3
%
N = input('Enter the number of resistors to simulate ');
M = input('Enter the number of histogram bins ');
R = input('Enter nominal resistance in ohms ');
P = input('Enter +- tolerance in % around nominal resistance ');
X = rand(1,N);
Y = R*(1 - P/100) + 2*(P/100)*R*X;
hist(Y,M),xlabel('resistance in ohms '),...
        ylabel('number of occurrences'),...
        title(['histogram for ' num2str(N), ' trials'])
```

histogram for 5000 trials

```
%       Computer Exercise 2-1
%
m = input('Enter the number of outcomes for event A ');
n = input('Enter the number of outcomes for event B ');
p = input('Enter number of outcomes common to A and B ');
PA = zeros(1,m);
PB = zeros(1,n);
PA_and_B = zeros(1,p);
PA = input('Enter probabilities for outcomes in A - sum <= 1 ');
PB = input('Enter probabilities for outcomes in B - sum <= 1 ');
Prob_A = sum(PA);
Prob_B = sum(PB);
fprintf('\n')
fprintf('Enter probabilities for outcomes in A union B ')
fprintf('Require sum <= 1 & sum >= %f \n',Prob_A+Prob_B-1)
fprintf('Also, sum <= P(A) = %f and <= P(B) = %f \n',Prob_A,Prob_B)
PA_and_B = input('');
Prob_A_and_B = sum(PA_and_B);
Prob_A_or_B = Prob_A + Prob_B - Prob_A_and_B;
```

```
PA_given_B = Prob_A_and_B/Prob_B;
PB_given_A = Prob_A_and_B/Prob_A;
fprintf('\n')
fprintf('P(A) = %5.3f; P(B) = %5.3f\n',Prob_A,Prob_B)
fprintf('\n')
fprintf('P(A and B) = %5.3f; P(A or B) = %5.3f\n',Prob_A_and_B,Prob_A_or_B)
fprintf('\n')
fprintf('P(A|B) = %5.3f; P(B|A) = %5.3f\n',PA_given_B,PB_given_A)
```

» ce2_1
Enter the number of outcomes for event A 3
Enter the number of outcomes for event B 4
Enter number of outcomes common to A and B 2
Enter probabilities for outcomes in A - sum <= 1 [.1 .05 .2]
Enter probabilities for outcomes in B - sum <= 1 [.05 .1 .1 .2]
Enter probabilities for outcomes in A union B Require sum <= 1 & sum >= -0.200000
Also, sum <= P(A) = 0.350000 and <= P(B) = 0.450000
[.1 .2]
P(A) = 0.350; P(B) = 0.450
P(A and B) = 0.300; P(A or B) = 0.500
P(A|B) = 0.667; P(B|A) = 0.857

```
%        Computer Exercise 2-2
%
%        To test proposition stated in exercise, enter all 6's for
%        vector of spot numbers sought and 1, 2, or 3 for minimum number of
%        matches for 6, 12, or 18 dice rolled.  The simulation will test for
%        any sequence of matches in order, e.g., 1 2 3 4 5 6 for 6 dies tossed.
%
N_dies = input('Enter number of dies to toss ');
spots = input('vector of spot numbers sought - one for each die tossed ');
no_matches_des = input('Enter minimum number of matches desired each toss ');
N_trials = input('Enter number of trials ');
count = 0;
L = length(spots);
for k = 1:N_trials
        X = rand(1,N_dies);
        spots_up = fix(6*X)+1;
        Y = spots_up - spots;
        no_matches_obt = L - nnz(Y);
        if no_matches_obt >= no_matches_des
                count = count + 1;
        end
```

```
end
disp(' ')
fprintf('The probability of the desired event is %f \n',count/N_trials)

» ce2_2
Enter number of dies to toss 6
vector of spot numbers sought - one for each die tossed [6 6 6 6 6 6]
Enter minimum number of matches desired each toss 1
Enter number of trials 1000
 The probability of the desired event is 0.667000


» ce2_2
Enter number of dies to toss 12
vector of spot numbers sought - one for each die tossed [6 6 6 6 6 6 6 6 6 6 6 6]
Enter minimum number of matches desired each toss 2
Enter number of trials 1000
 The probability of the desired event is 0.652000


» ce2_2
Enter number of dies to toss 18
vector of spot numbers sought - one for each die tossed [6 6 6 6 6 6 6 6 6 6 6 6 6 6 6 6 6 6]
Enter minimum number of matches desired each toss 3
Enter number of trials 1000
 The probability of the desired event is 0.623000


%       Computer Exercise 2-3
%       Case where host uses prior knowledge to reveal a goat
%
N_trials = input('Enter number of trials: ');
%       Host's curtain to pull back array; first index is "car behind
%       curtain no" and second index is "contestent's choice no"
W = zeros(3,3);
W(1,1) = fix(2*rand(1))+2;    % Random choice between 2 and 3
W(1,2) = 3;
W(1,3) = 2;
W(2,1) = 3;
W(2,2) = 3;     % Could be a random choice between 1 and 3
W(2,3) = 1;
W(3,1) = 2;
W(3,2) = 1;
W(3,3) = fix(2*rand(1))+1;    % Random choice between 1 and 2
%       Contestant switches to array; first index is contestent's
%       first choice and second index is host's curtain revealing
```

```
%        a goat
S(1,2) = 3;
S(1,3) = 2;
S(2,1) = 3;
S(2,3) = 1;
S(3,1) = 2;
S(3,2) = 1;
count1 = 0;
count2 = 0;
for k=1:N_trials
%        Generate number of curtain car is behind
         X = fix(3*rand(1))+1;
%        Generate number of curtain contestant picks
         Y = fix(3*rand(1))+1;
%        Generate host's curtain to pull back - assume knowledge used
         Z = W(X,Y);
         U = [X Y Z];
%        disp(U)                  % For checking
%        Assume don't switch
         if X == Y
                 count1 = count1 + 1;
         end
%        Assume switch
         Y_prime = S(Z,Y);
         if X == Y_prime
                 count2 = count2 + 1;
         end
end
disp(' ')
disp('Case where host uses prior knowledge to select between two remaining curtains:')
fprintf('  P(win car| contestant does not switch): %f \n',count1/N_trials)
fprintf('         P(win car| contestant switches): %f \n',count2/N_trials)


%        Computer Exercise 2-3b
%        Case where host makes random choice and reveals a goat
%        (cases where host randomly chooses car are thrown out)
%
N_trials = input('Enter number of trials: ');
%        Host's curtain to pull back array (car always behind curtain 1).
%        First index is "car behind curtain no" and
%        second index is "contestent's choice no".
%        Contestant randomly chooses 1, 2, or 3. Host never chooses
%        contestent's curtain and does not reveal a car.
```

```
W = zeros(3,3);
W(1,1) = fix(2*rand(1))+2;    %Host randomly picks 2 or 3
W(1,2) = 3;
W(1,3) = 2;
%       Contestant "switches to" array
S(1,2) = 3;
S(1,3) = 2;
S(2,1) = 3;
S(2,3) = 1;
S(3,1) = 2;
S(3,2) = 1;
count1 = 0;
count2 = 0;
for k=1:N_trials
%       Say car is always behind curtain 1
        X = 1;
%       Generate number of curtain contestant picks
        Y = fix(3*rand(1))+1;
%       Generate host's curtain to pull back - assume random
%       but goat revealed.
        if Y == 1
                R = rand(1);
                if R < 0.5
                        Z = 2;
                else
                        Z = 3;
                end
        elseif Y == 2
                R = rand(1);
                if R < 0.5
                        Z = 1;
                        N_trials =N_trials - 1;
                else
                        Z = 3;
                end
        elseif Y == 3
                Z = fix(2*rand(1))+1;
                if Z == 1
                        N_trials = N_trials - 1;
                end
        end
%       U = [X Y Z];
%       disp(U)
```

```
%        Assume don't switch
         if X == Y
                 count1 = count1 + 1;
         end
%        Assume switch
         Y_prime = S(Z,Y);
         if X == Y_prime
                 count2 = count2 + 1;
         end
end
disp(' ')
disp('Case where host makes random selection of two remaining curtains:')
fprintf('  P(win car | contestant does not switch): %f \n',count1/N_trials)
fprintf('      P(win car | contestant switches): %f \n',count2/N_trials)
```

» ce2_3

Enter number of trials: 5000

Case where host uses prior knowledge to select between two remaining curtains:
   P(win car | contestant does not switch): 0.345800
       P(win car | contestant switches): 0.654200
»
» ce2_3b

Enter number of trials: 5000

Case where host makes random selection of two remaining curtains:
   P(win car | contestant does not switch): 0.498042
       P(win car | contestant switches): 0.501958

```
%        Computer Exercise 3-1
%
clg
N_RV = input('Input the number of random variables to generate: ');
sigma2 = input('Input the sigma-squared parameter for the Rayleigh pdf: ');
n_bins = input('Input number of bins to use in histogram: ');
U = rand(1,N_RV);
V = sqrt(-2*sigma2*log(1-U));
del_x = (max(V) - min(V))/n_bins;
[n, x] = hist(V, n_bins);
n_norm = n/(N_RV*del_x);
y = 0:del_x:max(V);
```

```
fY = (1/sigma2)*y.*exp(-y.^2/(2*sigma2));
bar(x,n_norm,'-w'),grid, xlabel('x'),ylabel('f(x)'),...
title(['Comparison of histogram and theoretical pdf (dashed) for Rayleigh rvs; sigma^2 = ',
num2str(sigma2)])
hold
plot(y, fY,'--w')
```

» ce3_1
Input the number of random variables to generate: 10000
Input the sigma-squared parameter for the Rayleigh pdf: 4
Input number of bins to use in histogram: 25
Current plot held

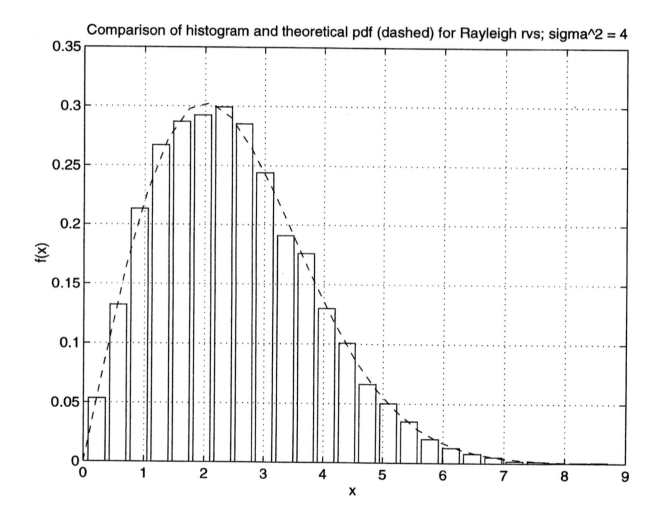

```
%       Computer Exercise 3-2
%
clg
N_RV = input('Input the number of random variables to generate: ');
alpha = input('Input the alpha parameter for the Cauchy pdf: ');
n_bins = input('Input the number of bins to use for the histogram: ');
U = rand(1,N_RV);
V = alpha*tan(pi*(U - 0.5));
del_y = alpha/10;
y = -7*alpha:del_y:7*alpha;
[n, x] = hist(V, y);
n_norm = n/(N_RV*del_y);
unit = ones(1,length(y));
fY = (alpha/pi)*unit./(y.^2 + alpha^2);
bar(y,n_norm,'-w'),grid, xlabel('y'),ylabel('f(y)'),axis([-7*alpha 7*alpha 0 max(n_norm)]),...
title(['Comparison of histogram and theoretical pdf (dashed) for Cauchy rvs; alpha = ',
num2str(alpha)])
hold
plot(y, fY,'--w')

» ce3_2
Input the number of random variables to generate: 5000
Input the alpha parameter for the Cauchy pdf: 4
Input the number of bins to use for the histogram: 15
Current plot held
```

Comparison of histogram and theoretical pdf (dashed) for Cauchy rvs; alpha = 4

127

```
%       Computer Exercise 3-3
%
N_trials = input('Enter the number of trials ');
p = input('Enter the the probability of success ');
X = zeros(1,N_trials);
U = rand(1,N_trials);
for i = 1:N_trials
        if U(i) < p
                X(i) = 1;
        end
end
mean_bin = N_trials*mean(X);
var_bin = N_trials*std(X)^2;
mean_theory = N_trials*p;
var_theory = N_trials*p*(1-p);
fprintf('The simulated mean of X is %6.2f and the theoretical mean is %6.2f \n',...
        mean_bin,mean_theory)
fprintf('The simulated variance of X is %6.2f and the theoretical variance is %6.2f \n',...
        var_bin,var_theory)
```

```
» ce3_3
Enter the number of trials 1000
Enter the the probability of success .4
The simulated mean of X is 419.00 and the theoretical mean is 400.00
The simulated variance of X is 243.68 and the theoretical variance is 240.00
»
» ce3_3
Enter the number of trials 5000
Enter the the probability of success .7
The simulated mean of X is 3521.00 and the theoretical mean is 3500.00
The simulated variance of X is 1041.72 and the theoretical variance is 1050.00
```

```
%       Computer Exercise 4-1
%
clg
N_trials = input('Enter the number of Gaussian random number pairs to generate ');
mean = input('Enter mean of Gaussian random numbers ');
var = input('Enter variance of Gaussian random numbers ');
M = input('Enter number of histogram bins to use ');
U = rand(1,N_trials);
V = rand(1,N_trials);
R = zeros(size(U));
X = zeros(size(X));
```

```
Y = zeros(size(Y));
R = sqrt(-log(U));
X = mean + sqrt(var)*R.*cos(2*pi*V);
Y = mean + sqrt(var)*R.*sin(2*pi*V);
subplot(2,1,1),hist(X,M),xlabel('x'),ylabel('no. of occurrences'),...
title('Histograms for X and Y Gaussian random number vectors'),grid
subplot(2,1,2),hist(Y,M),xlabel('y'),ylabel('no. of occurrences'),grid
```

» ce4_1
Enter the number of Gaussian random number pairs to generate 5000
Enter mean of Gaussian random numbers 4
Enter variance of Gaussian random numbers 2
Enter number of histogram bins to use 20

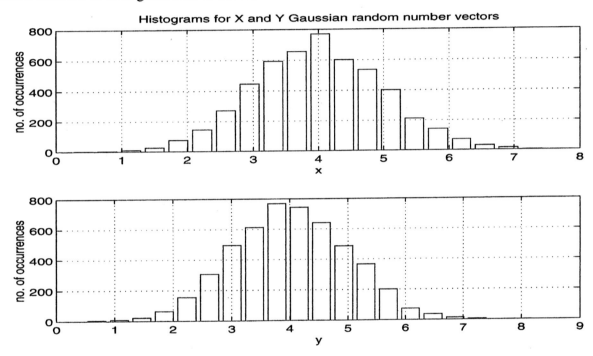

```
%        Computer Exercise 4-2
%
N_RV = input('Enter the number of Gaussian random numbers to generate ');
tau = input('Enter time separation between successive samples ');
alpha = input('Enter inverse corr. time, alpha, in rho = exp(-alpha*tau) ');
var = input('Enter variance of Gaussian random numbers ');
M = input('Enter number of histogram bins to use ');
rho_tau = exp(-alpha*tau);
U = rand(1);
```

129

```
V = rand(1);
R = sqrt(-log(U));
Y = sqrt(var)*R.*cos(2*pi*V);
X = zeros(1,N_RV);
t = zeros(1,N_RV);
X(1) = Y;
for k = 2:N_RV
        cond_mean = rho_tau*X(k-1);
        cond_var = var*(1 - rho_tau^2);
        U1 = rand(1);
        V1 = rand(1);
        R1 = sqrt(-log(U1));
        X(k) = cond_mean + sqrt(cond_var)*R1*cos(2*pi*V1);
        t(k) = tau*k;
end
subplot(2,1,1),plot(t,X),xlabel('time'),ylabel('amplitude'),grid,...
        title(['Correlated Gaussian random time series for intersample corr. =
',num2str(rho_tau)]),...
        axis([500 1000 -5 5])
subplot(2,1,2),hist(X,M),xlabel('k'),ylabel('no. of occurrences'),grid,...
        title('Histogram for correlated Gaussian random number sequence')
```

» ce4_2
Enter the number of Gaussian random numbers to generate 5000
Enter time separation between successive samples 1
Enter inverse corr. time, alpha, in rho = exp(-alpha*tau) 1
Enter variance of Gaussian random numbers 4
Enter number of histogram bins to use 15

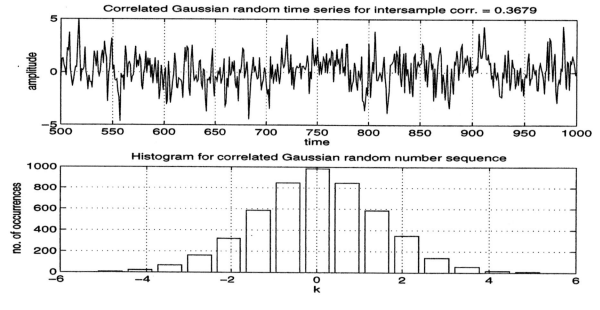

» ce4_2

Enter the number of Gaussian random numbers to generate 5000

Enter time separation between successive samples 1

Enter inverse corr. time, alpha, in rho = exp(-alpha*tau) 5

Enter variance of Gaussian random numbers 4

Enter number of histogram bins to use 15

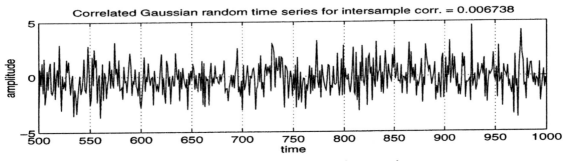

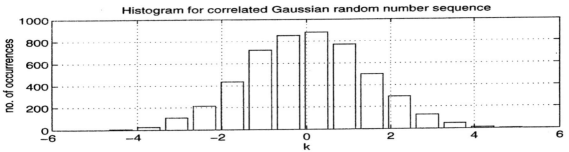

```
%        Computer Exercise 5-1
%
clg
N_trials = input('Enter the number of trials ');
alpha = input('Enter alpha parameter of Laplace density ');
M = input('Enter number of histogram bins to use ');
U = rand(1,N_trials);
X = zeros(size(U));
for k = 1:N_trials
        if U(k) <= 0.5
                X(k) = log(2*U(k));
        else
                X(k) = - log(2*(1 - U(k)));
        end
end
[nn, xx] = hist(X, M);
subplot(211), bar(xx, nn, 'w'),grid,xlabel('X value'),ylabel('counts'),...
        title('Histogram for Laplace rvs '),...
        axis([min(X)-5 max(X)+5 0 1.2*max(nn)])
y_inc = sort(X);
```

```
L = length(X);
J = 1:1:L;
J_norm = J/L;
J_norm(L+1) = J_norm(L);
y_inc(L+1) = y_inc(L) + 10;
[xy, yy] = stairs(y_inc, J_norm);
xy = [xy(1)-.001 xy']';
yy = [0 yy']';
subplot(212),plot(xy, yy, 'w'), grid, xlabel('X value'),ylabel('fraction <= abscissa'),...
        axis([min(X)-10 max(X)+10 0 1.1]), title('Empirical cdf for Laplace rvs ')
```

» ce5_1
Enter the number of trials 5000
Enter alpha parameter of Laplace density 2
Enter number of histogram bins to use 20

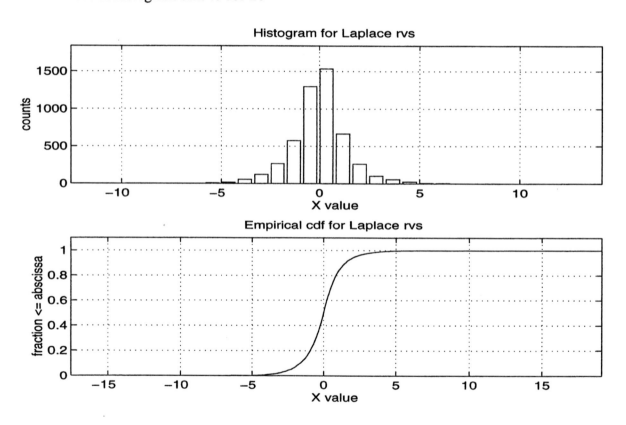

```
%       Computer Exercise 5-2
%
clg
N_trials = input('Enter the number of trials ');
```

132

```
sigma2 = input('Enter sigma^2 parameter of the Rayleigh density ');
M = input('Enter number of histogram bins to use ');
U = rand(1,N_trials);
V = sqrt(-2*sigma2*log(1-U));
[nn, xx] = hist(V, M);
subplot(211), bar(xx, nn, 'w'),grid,xlabel('V value'),ylabel('counts'),...
        title('Histogram for Rayleigh random variables '),...
        axis([min(V)-5 max(V)+5 0 1.2*max(nn)])
y_inc = sort(V);
L = length(V);
J = 1:1:L;
J_norm = J/L;
J_norm(L+1) = J_norm(L);
y_inc(L+1) = y_inc(L) + 10;
[xy, yy] = stairs(y_inc, J_norm);
xy = [xy(1)-.001 xy']';
yy = [0 yy']';
subplot(212),plot(xy, yy, 'w'), grid, xlabel('V value'),ylabel('fraction <= abscissa'),...
        axis([min(V)-10 max(V)+10 0 1.1]), title('Empirical cdf for Rayleigh random variables ')
```

» ce5_2
Enter the number of trials 5000
Enter sigma^2 parameter of the Rayleigh density 4

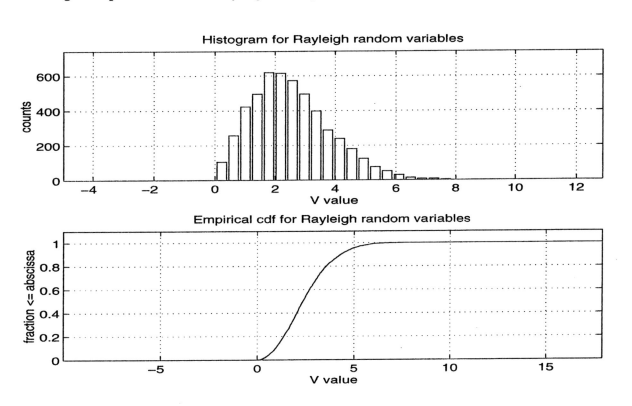

133

```
%       Computer Exercise 5-3
%
N=input('Enter of repetitions for simulation ');
tol_L=input('Enter per cent tolerance for inductor ');
tol_C=input('Enter per cent tolerance for capacitor ');
L_nom=input('Enter nominal value for inductor in millihenries ');
f0_nom=input('Enter desired nominal resonant frequency in kHz ');
C_est = 1/(4*pi^2*L_nom*10^(-3)*f0_nom^2*10^6)*10^6;
fprintf('For a res. freq. of %5.2f kHz the capacitance should be %5.2g microfarads \n',f0_nom,C_est);
C_nom=input('Enter nominal value for capacitor in microfarads ');
unit=ones(1,N);
%       Generate a 1XN vector of random numbers uniform in (-1,1)
delta1=2*rand(1,N)-1;
%       Form vector of random inductance values according to tolerance
L=L_nom*10^(-3)*(1+(tol_L/100)*delta1);
Lmax=max(L)*10^3;
Lmin=min(L)*10^3;
fprintf('The maximum and minimum inductance values are %6.3f & %6.3f mh, resp. \n', Lmax, Lmin);
%       Form vector of random capacitance values according to tolerance
delta2=2*rand(1,N)-1;
C=C_nom*10^(-6)*(1+(tol_C/100)*delta2);
Cmax=max(C)*10^6;
Cmin=min(C)*10^6;
fprintf('The maximum and minimum capacitance values are %6.3f & %6.3f microf, resp. \n', Cmax, Cmin);
%       Form vector of random resonant frequency values and plot histograms
f0=unit./(2*pi*sqrt(L.*C));
mean_f0 = mean(f0)*10^(-3);
std_dev_f0 = std(f0)*10^(-3);
[nL, xL] = hist(L*10^3,20);
deltaxL = xL(2)-xL(1);
[nC, xC] = hist(C*10^6,20);
deltaxC = xC(2)-xC(1);
[nf, xf] = hist(f0*10^(-3),20);
deltaxf = xf(2)-xf(1);
fprintf('The mean resonant frequency is %6.3f kHz\n',mean_f0);
fprintf('The standard deviation of the resonant frequency is %6.3f kHz\n',std_dev_f0);
subplot(3,1,1),bar(xL, nL/(N*deltaxL),'w'),xlabel('Inductance, millihenries'),...
        ylabel('No. of values'),title(['Histogram of inductance values for ' num2str(N) ' repetitions']),grid
subplot(3,1,2),bar(xC, nC/(N*deltaxC),'w'),xlabel('Capacitance, microfarads'),...
        ylabel('No. of values'),title('Histogram of capacitance values'),grid
subplot(3,1,3),bar(xf, nf/(N*deltaxf),'w'),xlabel('Resonant frequency, kHz'),...
        ylabel('No. of values'),title(['Histogram of resonant frequency values; smpl. mean res. freq. = '
num2str(mean_f0) ' Hz']),grid
» ce5_3
```

Enter of repetitions for simulation 5000
Enter per cent tolerance for inductor 10
Enter per cent tolerance for capacitor 10
Enter nominal value for inductor in millihenries 10
Enter desired nominal resonant frequency in kHz 10
For a res. freq. of 10.00 kHz the capacitance should be 0.025 microfarads
Enter nominal value for capacitor in microfarads .025
The maximum and minimum inductance values are 11.000 & 9.000 mh, resp.
The maximum and minimum capacitance values are 0.027 & 0.023 microf, resp.
The mean resonant frequency is 10.087 kHz
The standard deviation of the resonant frequency is 0.409 kHz

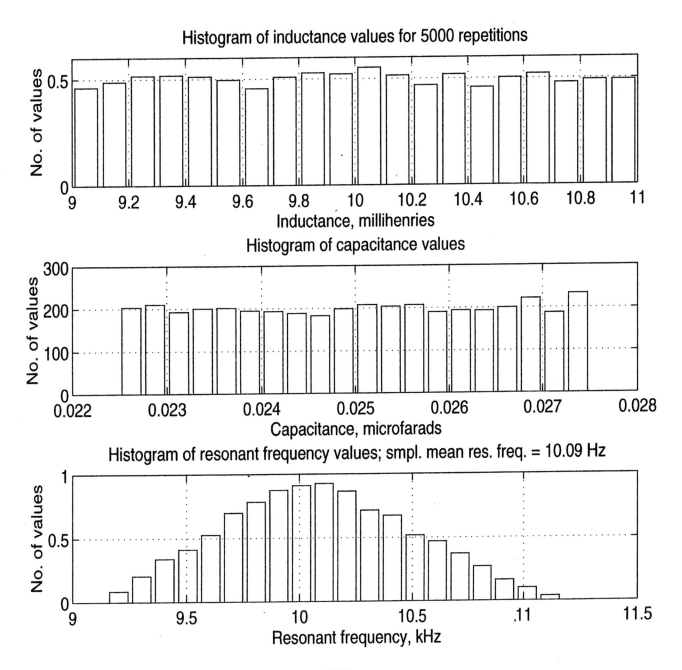

```
%       Computer Exercise 5-4
%
clg
mv=input('Enter vector (max. length = 4) of lot sizes ');
N=input('Enter total number of rivets ');
dia_nom=input('Enter nominal rivet diameter in millimeters ');
P_tol=input('Enter tolerance of diameter in per cent ');
%
%       Form array of random rivet diameters according to tolerance
%
K = length(mv);
for k = 1:K
m = mv(k);
n=N/m;
unit=ones(m,n);
X=2*rand(m,n)-unit;
dia_meas=dia_nom*(unit+(P_tol/100)*X);
lot_mean=mean(dia_meas);
mean_mean=mean(lot_mean);
std_dev_lot_mean=std(lot_mean);
lot_no=1:1:n;
UCL=mean_mean+3*std_dev_lot_mean*ones(1,n);
LCL=mean_mean-3*std_dev_lot_mean*ones(1,n);
fprintf('\n')
fprintf('UCL = %6.3f; LCL = %6.3f; sample mean = %6.3f; std dev of lot mean = %6.3f \n',...
UCL(1),LCL(1),mean_mean,std_dev_lot_mean)
subplot(2,2,k),plot(lot_no,lot_mean,'xw'),xlabel('Lot number'),ylabel('Diameter, mm'),...
        axis([0 max(lot_no) .99*LCL(1) 1.01*UCL(1)]),...
        title([ num2str(n) ' lots of size ' num2str(m) '; ' num2str(P_tol) ' % tolerance'])
hold
subplot(2,2,k),plot(lot_no,mean_mean*ones(1,n),'w')
subplot(2,2,k),plot(lot_no,UCL,'--w')
subplot(2,2,k),plot(lot_no,LCL,'--w')
end


» ce5_4
Enter vector (max. length = 4) of lot sizes [5 10 20 40]
Enter total number of rivets 1000
Enter nominal rivet diameter in millimeters 5
Enter tolerance of diameter in per cent 5
UCL = 5.194; LCL = 4.810; sample mean = 5.002; std dev of lot mean = 0.064
Current plot held
UCL = 5.146; LCL = 4.853; sample mean = 5.000; std dev of lot mean = 0.049
Current plot held
UCL = 5.106; LCL = 4.908; sample mean = 5.007; std dev of lot mean = 0.033
```

Current plot held
UCL = 5.082; LCL = 4.928; sample mean = 5.005; std dev of lot mean = 0.026
Current plot held

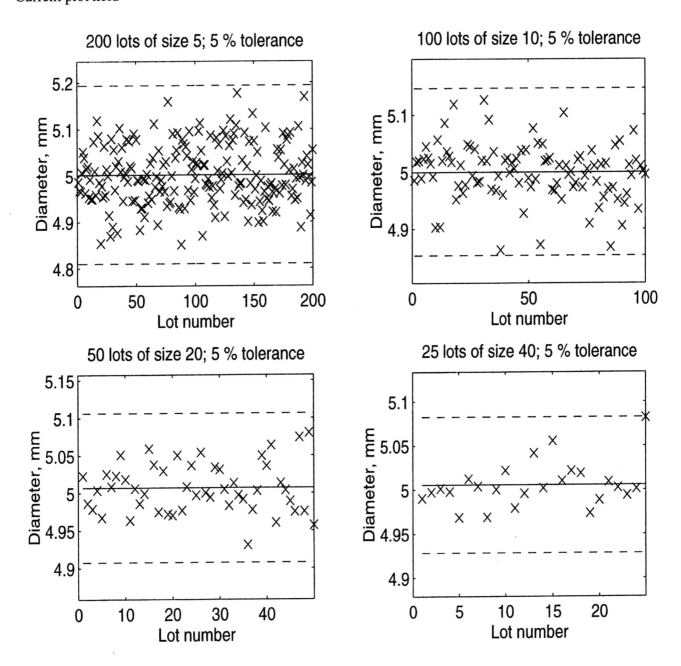

```
%       Computer Exercise 6-1
%
mu = input('Enter the mean of the Gaussian random variables ');
sigma2 = input('Enter the variance of the Gaussian random variables ');
N = input('Enter the number of Gaussian random variables to generate ');
X = sqrt(sigma2)*randn(1,N) + mu;
x_bar = (1/N)*sum(X);
sigma2_hat_nm = (1/N)*sum((X - mu).^2);
sigma2_hat_um = (1/(N - 1))*sum((X - x_bar).^2);
fprintf('\n');
fprintf('The estimate of the mean is %f \n', x_bar);
fprintf('The estimate of the variance, mean unknown, is %f \n', sigma2_hat_um);
fprintf('The estimate of the variance, mean known, is %f \n', sigma2_hat_nm);
```

» ce6_1
Enter the mean of the Gaussian random variables 4
Enter the variance of the Gaussian random variables 6
Enter the number of Gaussian random variables to generate 10000

The estimate of the mean is 3.998432
The estimate of the variance, mean unknown, is 6.187819
The estimate of the variance, mean known, is 6.187202

```
%       Computer Exercise 6-2
%
clg
mu = input('Enter the mean of the Gaussian random variables ');
sigma2 = input('Enter the variance of the Gaussian random variables ');
n = input('Enter the number of Gaussian random variables per batch ');
Nv = input('Enter the vector (max = 4) of number of batches to generate ');
K = length(Nv);
for k = 1:K
N = Nv(k);
X = sqrt(sigma2)*randn(n,N) + mu;
x_bar = (1/n)*sum(X);
sigma2_hat = (std(X)).^2;
fprintf('\n');
true_mean = mu;              %       True mean of the sample mean
true_var = sigma2/n;  %       True variance of the sample mean
true_std_dev = sqrt(true_var);
%
%       set up abscissa values for comparing histogram of means with true pdf
%
```

```
delta = true_std_dev/10;
x_start = true_mean - 3*true_std_dev;
x_stop = true_mean + 3*true_std_dev;
x = [x_start:delta:x_stop];
fx = exp(-(x-true_mean).^2/(2*true_var))/sqrt(2*pi*true_var);
[m,y] = hist(x_bar,x);
NN = sum(m);                    %       The total number of counts in all bins
norm = NN*delta;                %       The normalizing factor to make the histogram
                                %       match the pdf of the sample means.
peak = max(m/norm);
subplot(2,2,k),bar(x,m/(NN*delta), 'w'),grid,...
        axis([x_start-.1 x_stop+.1 0 peak]),...
        xlabel('Sample mean value'),...
        ylabel('Norm. freq. of occurence'),...
        title([num2str(N), ' batches of ',num2str(n), ' samples']),...
if k==1
        text(x_start-.05, peak-.06, 'true mean of samples = '),...
        text(x_start+55*delta, peak-.06, num2str(mu)),...
        text(x_start-.05, peak-.16, 'true var of samples = '),...
        text(x_start+55*delta, peak-.16, num2str(sigma2))
end
hold
subplot(2,2,k),plot(x,fx,'+w')
end


» ce6_2
Enter the mean of the Gaussian random variables 4
Enter the variance of the Gaussian random variables 6
Enter the number of Gaussian random variables per batch 25
Enter the vector (max = 4) of number of batches to generate [100 500 1000 2000]


» ce6_2
Enter the mean of the Gaussian random variables 4
Enter the variance of the Gaussian random variables 6
Enter the number of Gaussian random variables per batch 50
Enter the vector (max = 4) of number of batches to generate [100 500 1000 2000]
```

139

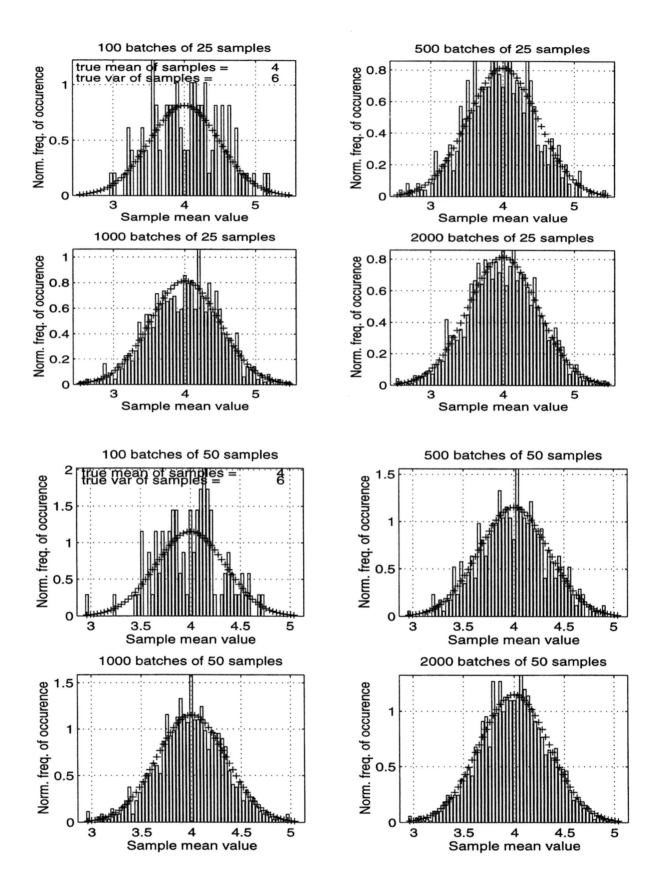

```
%       Computer Exercise 6-3
%
mu = input('Enter the true mean of the Gaussian random variable ');
sigma2 = input('Enter the true variance of the Gaussian random variable ');
n = input('Enter the number of RVs in sample mean ');
N = input('Enter the number of trials ');
betav = input('Enter vector of confidence levels in per cent (90, 95, 98, or 99) ');
K = length(betav);
for k = 1:K
beta = betav(k);
if beta == 90
        zc = 1.645;
elseif beta == 95
        zc = 1.96;
elseif beta == 98
        zc = 2.326;
elseif beta == 99
        zc = 2.576;
end
X = sqrt(sigma2)*randn(n,N) + mu;
mu_X_hat = (1/n)*sum(X);
lower_limit = mu_X_hat - zc*sqrt(sigma2)/sqrt(n);
upper_limit = mu_X_hat + zc*sqrt(sigma2)/sqrt(n);
count = 0;
for k = 1:N
        if mu <= upper_limit(k) & mu >= lower_limit(k)
                count = count + 1;
        end
end
conf = count*100/N;
fprintf('\n')
fprintf('The specified confidence level is %5.1f and the experimental one is %6.2f \n', beta, conf);
end
```

» ce6_3
Enter the true mean of the Gaussian random variable 4
Enter the true variance of the Gaussian random variable 6
Enter the number of RVs in sample mean 10
Enter the number of trials 5000
Enter vector of confidence levels in per cent (90, 95, 98, or 99) [90 95 98 99]

The specified confidence level is 90.0 and the experimental one is 90.26
The specified confidence level is 95.0 and the experimental one is 94.90

The specified confidence level is 98.0 and the experimental one is 98.00
The specified confidence level is 99.0 and the experimental one is 98.88

```
%         Computer Exercise 6-4
%
mu = input('Enter the true mean of the Gaussian random variable ');
sigma2 = input('Enter the true variance of the Gaussian random variable ');
n = input('Enter the number of RVs in sample variance (10, 20, 30) ');
N = input('Enter the number of trials ');
betav = input('Enter vector of confidence levels in per cent (90, 95, 98, or 99) ');
X = sqrt(sigma2)*randn(n,N) + mu;
sigma_X_hat2 = std(X).^2;
K = length(betav);
fprintf('Confidence intervals for the variance with the mean known: \n');
for k = 1:K
beta = betav(k);
if beta == 90
        if n == 10
                delta = 18.307;
                gamma = 3.94;
        elseif n == 20
                delta = 31.41;
                gamma = 10.851;
        elseif n == 30
                delta = 43.773;
                gamma = 18.493;
        end
elseif beta == 95
        if n == 10
                delta = 20.483;
                gamma = 3.247;
        elseif n == 20
                delta = 34.17;
                gamma = 9.591;
        elseif n == 30
                delta = 46.979;
                gamma = 16.791;
        end
elseif beta == 98
        if n == 10
                delta = 23.209;
                gamma = 2.558;
        elseif n == 20
```

```
                delta = 37.566;
                gamma = 8.26;
        elseif n == 30
                delta = 50.892;
                gamma = 14.953;
        end
elseif beta == 99
        if n == 10
                delta = 25.188;
                gamma = 2.156;
        elseif n == 20
                delta = 39.997;
                gamma = 7.434;
        elseif n == 30
                delta = 53.672;
                gamma = 13.787;
        end
end
lower_limit = n*sigma_X_hat2/delta;
upper_limit = n*sigma_X_hat2/gamma;
count = 0;
for k = 1:N
        if sigma2 <= upper_limit(k) & sigma2 >= lower_limit(k)
                count = count + 1;
        end
end
conf = count*100/N;
fprintf('\n')
fprintf('The specified confidence level is %5.1f and the experimental one is %6.2f \n', beta, conf);
end


» ce6_4
Enter the true mean of the Gaussian random variable 4
Enter the true variance of the Gaussian random variable 6
Enter the number of RVs in sample variance (10, 20, 30) 10
Enter the number of trials 5000
Enter vector of confidence levels in per cent (90, 95, 98, or 99) [90 95 98 99]

Confidence intervals for the variance with the mean known:
The specified confidence level is  90.0 and the experimental one is  88.16
The specified confidence level is  95.0 and the experimental one is  93.66
The specified confidence level is  98.0 and the experimental one is  97.28
The specified confidence level is  99.0 and the experimental one is  98.54
```

143

» ce6_4
Enter the true mean of the Gaussian random variable 4
Enter the true variance of the Gaussian random variable 6
Enter the number of RVs in sample variance (10, 20, 30) 20
Enter the number of trials 5000
Enter vector of confidence levels in per cent (90, 95, 98, or 99) [90 95 98 99]

Confidence intervals for the variance with the mean known:
The specified confidence level is 90.0 and the experimental one is 88.76
The specified confidence level is 95.0 and the experimental one is 94.02
The specified confidence level is 98.0 and the experimental one is 97.18
The specified confidence level is 99.0 and the experimental one is 98.58
»
» ce6_4
Enter the true mean of the Gaussian random variable 4
Enter the true variance of the Gaussian random variable 6
Enter the number of RVs in sample variance (10, 20, 30) 30
Enter the number of trials 5000
Enter vector of confidence levels in per cent (90, 95, 98, or 99) [90 95 98 99]

Confidence intervals for the variance with the mean known:
The specified confidence level is 90.0 and the experimental one is 89.24
The specified confidence level is 95.0 and the experimental one is 94.30
The specified confidence level is 98.0 and the experimental one is 97.58
The specified confidence level is 99.0 and the experimental one is 98.66

```
%       Computer Exercise 6-5
%
mu = input('Enter the true mean of the Gaussian random variable ');
sigma2 = input('Enter the true variance of the Gaussian random variable ');
n = input('Enter the number of RVs in sample variance (10, 20, 30) ');
N = input('Enter the number of trials ');
betav = input('Enter vector of confidence levels in per cent (90, 95, 98, or 99) ');
X = sqrt(sigma2)*randn(n,N) + mu;
sigma_X_hat2 = std(X).^2;
K = length(betav);
fprintf('Confidence intervals for the variance with the mean unknown: \n');
for k = 1:K
beta = betav(k);
if beta == 90
        if n == 10
                delta = 16.919;
                gamma = 3.325;
```

```
            elseif n == 20
                    delta = 30.144;
                    gamma = 10.117;
            elseif n == 30
                    delta = 42.557;
                    gamma = 17.708;
            end
    elseif beta == 95
            if n == 10
                    delta = 19.023;
                    gamma = 2.7;
            elseif n == 20
                    delta = 32.853;
                    gamma = 8.906;
            elseif n == 30
                    delta = 45.722;
                    gamma = 16.047;
            end
    elseif beta == 98
            if n == 10
                    delta = 21.666;
                    gamma = 2.088;
            elseif n == 20
                    delta = 36.191;
                    gamma = 7.632;
            elseif n == 30
                    delta = 49.588;
                    gamma = 14.256;
            end
    elseif beta == 99
            if n == 10
                    delta = 23.589;
                    gamma = 1.735;
            elseif n == 20
                    delta = 38.582;
                    gamma = 6.843;
            elseif n == 30
                    delta = 52.336;
                    gamma = 13.121;
            end
    end
    lower_limit = (n-1)*sigma_X_hat2/delta;
    upper_limit = (n-1)*sigma_X_hat2/gamma;
```

145

```
count = 0;
for k = 1:N
        if sigma2 <= upper_limit(k) & sigma2 >= lower_limit(k)
                count = count + 1;
        end
end
conf = count*100/N;
fprintf('\n')
fprintf('The specified confidence level is %5.1f and the experimental one is %6.2f \n', beta, conf);
end
```

» ce6_5
Enter the true mean of the Gaussian random variable 4
Enter the true variance of the Gaussian random variable 6
Enter the number of RVs in sample variance (10, 20, 30) 10
Enter the number of trials 5000
Enter vector of confidence levels in per cent (90, 95, 98, or 99) [90 95 98 99]

Confidence intervals for the variance with the mean unknown
The specified confidence level is 90.0 and the experimental one is 90.16
The specified confidence level is 95.0 and the experimental one is 94.88
The specified confidence level is 98.0 and the experimental one is 98.06
The specified confidence level is 99.0 and the experimental one is 99.14
»
» ce6_5
Enter the true mean of the Gaussian random variable 4
Enter the true variance of the Gaussian random variable 6
Enter the number of RVs in sample variance (10, 20, 30) 20
Enter the number of trials 5000
Enter vector of confidence levels in per cent (90, 95, 98, or 99) [90 95 98 99]

Confidence intervals for the variance with the mean unknown:
The specified confidence level is 90.0 and the experimental one is 90.20
The specified confidence level is 95.0 and the experimental one is 95.26
The specified confidence level is 98.0 and the experimental one is 97.94
The specified confidence level is 99.0 and the experimental one is 98.90
»
» ce6_5
Enter the true mean of the Gaussian random variable 4
Enter the true variance of the Gaussian random variable 6
Enter the number of RVs in sample variance (10, 20, 30) 30
Enter the number of trials 5000
Enter vector of confidence levels in per cent (90, 95, 98, or 99) [90 95 98 99]

Confidence intervals for the variance with the mean unknown:
The specified confidence level is 90.0 and the experimental one is 90.28
The specified confidence level is 95.0 and the experimental one is 94.84
The specified confidence level is 98.0 and the experimental one is 98.14
The specified confidence level is 99.0 and the experimental one is 99.24

```
%       Computer Exercise 6-6
%
mu = input('Enter the true mean of the Gaussian random variable ');
sigma2 = input('Enter the true variance of the Gaussian random variable ');
n = input('Enter the number of RVs in sample variance (10, 20, 30) ');
N = input('Enter the number of trials ');
betav = input('Enter vector of confidence levels in per cent (90, 95, 98, or 99) ');
X = sqrt(sigma2)*randn(n,N) + mu;
mu_X_hat = (1/n)*sum(X);
sigma_X_hat2 = std(X).^2;
K = length(betav);
fprintf(' \n');
fprintf('Confidence intervals for the mean with the variance unknown: \n');
for k = 1:K
beta = betav(k);
if beta == 90
        if n == 10
                tc = 1.834;
        elseif n == 20
                tc = 1.73;
        elseif n == 30
                tc = 1.312;
        end
elseif beta == 95
        if n == 10
                tc = 2.263;
        elseif n == 20
                tc = 2.094;
        elseif n == 30
                tc = 2.046;
        end
elseif beta == 98
        if n == 10
                tc = 2.822;
        elseif n == 20
                tc = 2.54;
        elseif n == 30
```

147

```
                    tc = 2.463;
            end
elseif beta == 99
        if n == 10
                tc = 3.25;
        elseif n == 20
                tc = 2.861;
        elseif n == 30
                tc = 2.757;
        end
end
lower_limit = mu_X_hat - tc*sqrt(sigma_X_hat2/n);
upper_limit = mu_X_hat + tc*sqrt(sigma_X_hat2/n);
count = 0;
for k = 1:N
        if mu <= upper_limit(k) & mu >= lower_limit(k)
                count = count + 1;
        end
end
conf = count*100/N;
fprintf('\n')
fprintf('The specified confidence level is %5.1f and the experimental one is %6.2f \n', beta, conf);
end
```

» ce6_6
Enter the true mean of the Gaussian random variable 4
Enter the true variance of the Gaussian random variable 6
Enter the number of RVs in sample variance (10, 20, 30) 10
Enter the number of trials 5000
Enter vector of confidence levels in per cent (90, 95, 98, or 99) [90 95 98 99]

Confidence intervals for the mean with the variance unknown:
The specified confidence level is 90.0 and the experimental one is 89.88
The specified confidence level is 95.0 and the experimental one is 95.16
The specified confidence level is 98.0 and the experimental one is 98.00
The specified confidence level is 99.0 and the experimental one is 99.16
»
» ce6_6
Enter the true mean of the Gaussian random variable 4
Enter the true variance of the Gaussian random variable 6
Enter the number of RVs in sample variance (10, 20, 30) 20
Enter the number of trials 5000
Enter vector of confidence levels in per cent (90, 95, 98, or 99) [90 95 98 99]

148

Confidence intervals for the mean with the variance unknown:
The specified confidence level is 90.0 and the experimental one is 90.00
The specified confidence level is 95.0 and the experimental one is 95.30
The specified confidence level is 98.0 and the experimental one is 98.06
The specified confidence level is 99.0 and the experimental one is 98.92
»

» ce6_6
Enter the true mean of the Gaussian random variable .4
Enter the true variance of the Gaussian random variable 6
Enter the number of RVs in sample variance (10, 20, 30) 30
Enter the number of trials 5000
Enter vector of confidence levels in per cent (90, 95, 98, or 99) [90 95 98 99]

Confidence intervals for the mean with the variance unknown:
The specified confidence level is 90.0 and the experimental one is 80.64
The specified confidence level is 95.0 and the experimental one is 95.22
The specified confidence level is 98.0 and the experimental one is 97.96
The specified confidence level is 99.0 and the experimental one is 99.02


```
%        Computer Exercise 6-7
%
m = input('Enter the mean of signal component ');
sigma2 = input('Enter the variance of the signal component ');
sigman2 = input('Enter the variance of the noise samples ');
n = input('Enter the number of samples per estimate ');
N = input('Enter the number of trials ');
Y = sqrt(sigma2)*randn(1,1) + m;
N_noise = sqrt(sigman2)*randn(n,N);
X = Y +N_noise;
x_bar = (1/n)*sum(X);
sigmaP2 = 1/(n/sigman2 + 1/sigma2);
K1 = n*sigmaP2/sigman2;
K2 = sigmaP2/sigma2;
est_Y = K1*x_bar + K2*m;
var_est_Y = std(est_Y).^2;
fprintf(' \n');
fprintf('The theoretical variance of the estimate is %5.2f; \n',sigmaP2);
fprintf('             the Monte Carlo estimate is %5.2f \n',var_est_Y)
```

» ce6_7
Enter the mean of signal component 6
Enter the variance of the signal component 4
Enter the variance of the noise samples 2

Enter the number of samples per estimate 10
Enter the number of trials 5000

The theoretical variance of the estimate is 0.19;
the Monte Carlo estimate is 0.18
»
» ce6_7
Enter the mean of signal component 6
Enter the variance of the signal component 2
Enter the variance of the noise samples 10
Enter the number of samples per estimate 25
Enter the number of trials 5000

The theoretical variance of the estimate is 0.33;
the Monte Carlo estimate is 0.28

```
%        Computer Exercise 7-1
%
A_sigma = input('Enter the ratio of the signal component to noise std dev ');
p = input('Enter the prior probability of signal present ');
q = 1 - p;
thres_opt = -log(p/q)/A_sigma + A_sigma/2
T_sigmav = input('Enter the vector of ratio of the threshold to noise std dev ');
N = input('Enter the number of trials ');
K = length(T_sigmav);
for kk = 1:K
threshold = T_sigmav(kk);
AA = zeros(1, N);
unit = zeros(1, N);
N_noise = zeros(1, N);
for k = 1:N
        if rand(1) <= p
                AA(k) = A_sigma;
                unit(k) = 1;
        end
end
N_noise = randn(1,N);          %With normalized threshold & signal, noise can be unit variance
Z = AA +N_noise;
miss = 0;
false = 0;
N_sig = 0;
for k = 1:N
        if Z(k) >= threshold & AA(k) == 0
```

```
                    false = false + 1;
            elseif Z(k) <= threshold & AA(k) > 0
                    miss = miss + 1;
            end
            if AA(k) > 0
                    N_sig = N_sig + 1;
            end
    end
end
N_no_sig = N - N_sig;
p_rel_freq = sum(unit)/N;
q_rel_freq = 1 - p_rel_freq;
rel_freq_miss = miss/N_sig;
rel_freq_false = false/N_no_sig;
P_false_alarm = qfn(threshold);
P_miss = qfn((A_sigma - threshold));
rel_freq_cost = p_rel_freq*rel_freq_miss+q_rel_freq*rel_freq_false;
cost = p*P_miss + q*P_false_alarm;
fprintf(' \n');
fprintf('For a normalized threshold of %6.3f, the false alarm rel. freq. is %6.3g; \n',
threshold,rel_freq_false);
fprintf('                  the theoretical probability of false alarm is %6.3g; \n', P_false_alarm);
fprintf('                         the miss relative frequency is %6.3g; \n', rel_freq_miss);
fprintf('                  the theoretical probability of a miss is %6.3g; \n', P_miss);
fprintf('                    the rel. frequency cost per decision is %6.3g; \n', rel_freq_cost)
fprintf('                  the theoretical average cost per decision is %6.3g. \n', cost)
end
```

» ce7_1
Enter the ratio of the signal component to noise std dev 6
Enter the prior probability of signal present .3
thres_opt = 3.1412   *(this is an output)*
Enter the vector of ratio of the threshold to noise std dev [0 1 2 3 4 5 6]
Enter the number of trials 5000

For a normalized threshold of 0.000, the false alarm rel. freq. is	0.509;
the theoretical probability of false alarm is	0.5;
the miss relative frequency is	0;
the theoretical probability of a miss is	9.87e-010;
the rel. frequency cost per decision is	0.351;
the theoretical average cost per decision is	0.35.

For a normalized threshold of 1.000, the false alarm rel. freq. is	0.158;
the theoretical probability of false alarm is	0.159;

the miss relative frequency is   0;
the theoretical probability of a miss is   2.87e-007;
the rel. frequency cost per decision is   0.111;
the theoretical average cost per decision is   0.111.

For a normalized threshold of 2.000, the false alarm rel. freq. is   0.0224;
the theoretical probability of false alarm is   0.0228;
the miss relative frequency is   0;
the theoretical probability of a miss is   0.0000318;
the rel. frequency cost per decision is   0.0156;
the theoretical average cost per decision is   0.0159.

For a normalized threshold of 3.000, the false alarm rel. freq. is   0.000568;
the theoretical probability of false alarm is   0.00135;
the miss relative frequency is   0.00203;
the theoretical probability of a miss is   0.00135;
the rel. frequency cost per decision is   0.001;
the theoretical average cost per decision is   0.00135.

For a normalized threshold of 4.000, the false alarm rel. freq. is   0.000289;
the theoretical probability of false alarm is   0.0000318;
the miss relative frequency is   0.026;
the theoretical probability of a miss is   0.0228;
the rel. frequency cost per decision is   0.0082;
the theoretical average cost per decision is   0.00685.

For a normalized threshold of 5.000, the false alarm rel. freq. is   0;
the theoretical probability of false alarm is   2.87e-007;
the miss relative frequency is   0.165;
the theoretical probability of a miss is   0.159;
the rel. frequency cost per decision is   0.0496;
the theoretical average cost per decision is   0.0476.

For a normalized threshold of 6.000, the false alarm rel. freq. is   0;
the theoretical probability of false alarm is   9.87e-010;
the miss relative frequency is   0.513;
the theoretical probability of a miss is   0.5;
the rel. frequency cost per decision is   0.153;
the theoretical average cost per decision is   0.15.

```
%          Computer Exercise 7-2
%
clg
L = input('Enter the nominal length of the bar in cm ');
sigma2 = input('Enter the variance of the measurement error in cm^2 ');
n = input('Enter the number of measurements made on a bar ');
N = input('Enter the number of trials ');
alpha = input('Enter probability of type I error ');
N_meas = sqrt(sigma2)*randn(n,N);
meas = L + N_meas;
sample_mean = 1/n*sum(meas);
%
%          Assume hypothesis 0 is true
%
mu0 = L;
Y0 = (sample_mean - mu0)/(sqrt(sigma2/n));
c = sqrt(2)*erfinv(1 - alpha);
count0 = 0;
for k = 1:N
        if Y0(k) > c | Y0(k) < -c
                count0 = count0 + 1;
        end
end
rel_freq_type_I = count0/N;
fprintf('\n')
fprintf('The confidence interval boundary is %5.2f \n',c);
fprintf('The relative frequency of the type I error is %5.2f \n',rel_freq_type_I)
%
%          Assume hypothesis 0 is false (1 true) and mean
%          length of bar is mu not equal to L.  Plot OC curve.
%
mu = zeros(1,51);
beta = zeros(1,51);
for i = 1:51
        mu(i) = 0.95*L + (i-1)*L/500;
        mu1 = (mu(i) - mu0)/sqrt(sigma2/n);
        Y1 = mu1 + randn(1,N);
        count1 = 0;
        for k = 1:N
                if Y1(k) > -c & Y1(k) < c
                        count1 = count1 + 1;
                end
        end
```

153

```
        beta(i) = count1/N;
end
arg1 = c-(mu-L)*sqrt(n)/sqrt(sigma2);
arg2 = c+(mu-L)*sqrt(n)/sqrt(sigma2);
one_minus_beta_thy = qfn(arg1) + qfn(arg2);
plot(mu,1-beta,'-w'),grid,xlabel('True mean length'),...
        ylabel('1 - probability of type 2 error'),...
        title(['OC curve, - - = theory; bar length = ', num2str(L),' units; ',num2str(n),' noisy
measurements of variance = ',num2str(sigma2)])
hold
plot(mu,one_minus_beta_thy,'--w')
print c:\probab\compex\ce7_2a -dps
```

» ce7_2
Enter the nominal length of the bar in cm 10
Enter the variance of the measurement error in cm^2 .1
Enter the number of measurements made on a bar 10
Enter the number of trials 1000
Enter probability of type I error .05

The confidence interval boundary is 1.96
The relative frequency of the type I error is 0.04
Current plot held

» ce7_2
Enter the nominal length of the bar in cm 10
Enter the variance of the measurement error in cm^2 .1
Enter the number of measurements made on a bar 50
Enter the number of trials 1000
Enter probability of type I error .05

The confidence interval boundary is 1.96
The relative frequency of the type I error is 0.05
Current plot held

154

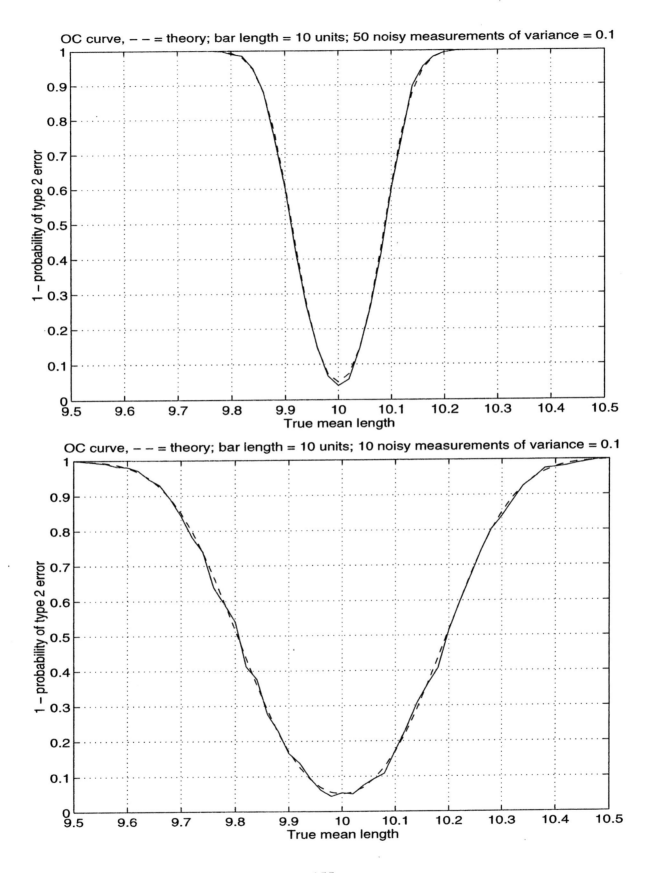

155

```
%        Computer Exercise 7-3
%
sigma2 = input('Enter the variance of confusion noise ');
N = input('Enter the number of trials ');
N_meas = sqrt(sigma2)*randn(1,N);
X = rand(1,N);
Y = fix(6*X) + 1;
data = ones(6,1)*(Y + N_meas);
true = (ones(N,1)*[1 2 3 4 5 6])';
[y,k] = min(abs(data-true));
%disp(Y)
%disp(k)
%disp(y)
wrong_guesses = sum(abs(sign(Y - k)));
right_guesses = N - wrong_guesses;
winnings = right_guesses - wrong_guesses;
fprintf('\n')
fprintf('The winnings are $ %6.2f in %6.0f trials\n',winnings, N)
```

» ce7_3
Enter the variance of confusion noise 10
Enter the number of trials 1000
The winnings are $ -450.00 in   1000 trials

» ce7_3
Enter the variance of confusion noise 5
Enter the number of trials 1000
The winnings are $ -382.00 in   1000 trials

» ce7_3
Enter the variance of confusion noise 1
Enter the number of trials 1000
The winnings are $ -94.00 in   1000 trials

» ce7_3
Enter the variance of confusion noise .5
Enter the number of trials 1000
The winnings are $ 192.00 in   1000 trials

```
%       Computer Exercise 8-1
%
N = input('Enter the number of trials ');
disp('Choose type of system ');
        disp('   1 = series');
        disp('   2 = parallel');
i_series_par = input('Enter 1 or 2 ');
if i_series_par == 1
        n_series = input('Enter number of subsystems in series ');
        R_series = input('Enter vector of reliabilities of the series systems ');
elseif i_series_par == 2
        n_parallel = input('Enter number of subsystems in parallel ');
        R_parallel = input('Enter vector of reliabilities of the parallel systems ');
end
if i_series_par == 1
        series_succ = rand(N,n_series);
        series_rel_matrix = ones(N,1)*R_series;
        succ_matrix = sign((series_rel_matrix - series_succ)')+1;
        succeed = all(succ_matrix);
        system_reliability = sum(succeed)/N;
        disp(' ')
        disp('Simulated series system reliability')
        disp(system_reliability)
        disp('Theoretical series system reliability')
        disp(prod(R_series))
elseif i_series_par == 2
        paral_fail = rand(N,n_parallel);
        parallel_fail_matrix = 1 - ones(N,1)*R_parallel;
        fail_matrix = sign((parallel_fail_matrix - paral_fail)')+1;
        fail = all(fail_matrix);
        system_reliability = 1 - sum(fail)/N;
        disp(' ')
        disp('Simulated parallel system reliability')
        disp(system_reliability)
        disp('Theoretical parallel system reliability')
        disp(1-prod((1-R_series)))
end

» ce8_1
Enter the number of trials 5000
Choose type of system
        1 = series
        2 = parallel
```

Enter 1 or 2 1
Enter number of subsystems in series 4
Enter vector of reliabilities of the series systems [.8 .9 .6 .95]

Simulated series system reliability
  4.1680e-001
Theoretical series system reliability
  4.1040e-001

» ce8_1
Enter the number of trials 5000
Choose type of system
        1 = series
        2 = parallel
Enter 1 or 2 2
Enter number of subsystems in parallel 4
Enter vector of reliabilities of the parallel systems [.8 .9 .6 .95]

Simulated parallel system reliability
  9.9960e-001
Theoretical parallel system reliability
  9.9960e-001

```
%       Computer Exercise 8-2
%
clg
lambda = input('Enter lambda for the standby systems ');
n = input('Enter the maximum number of standby systems ');
t = [0:(10*lambda)^(-1):20/lambda];
reliability = zeros(size(t));
N = length(t);
lambda_t = lambda*t;
for j = 1:n
        if j == 1
                reliability = exp(-lambda_t);
        else
                factor = ones(j,N);
                for k = 2:j
                        factor(k,:) = (lambda_t.^(k - 1))/prod(1:k - 1);
                end
                reliability = sum(factor).*exp(-lambda_t);
        end
        plot(lambda_t,reliability,'-w'),xlabel('lambda*t'),...
```

```
        ylabel('reliability'),text(lambda_t(N/5),reliability(N/5), num2str(j)),... ·
        title(['Reliabilities for n standby systems; n = 1 - ', num2str(n)])
        if j == 1
                hold on
                grid on
        end
end
```

» ce8_2
Enter lambda for the standby systems 10
Enter the maximum number of standby systems 9

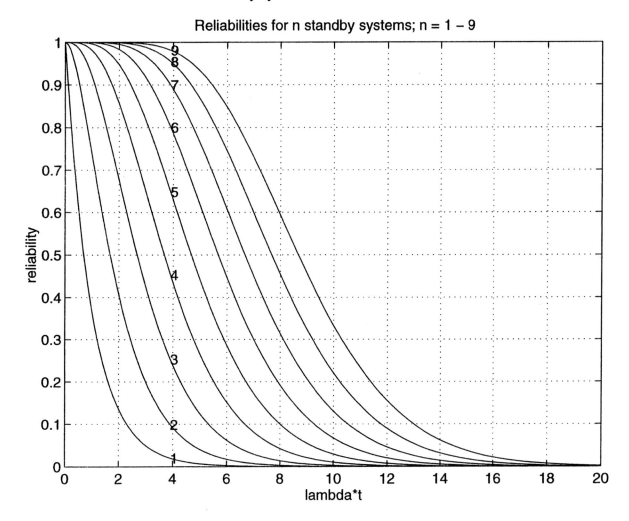

```
%        Computer Exercise 8-3
%
clg
c=input('Enter c parameter ');
m=input('Enter m parameter ');
N=input('Enter total random numbers to generate ');
M=input('Enter number of histogram bins ');
Y=rand(1,N);
T=c*(-log(Y+.0001)).^(1/m);
TT=sort(T);
[nn yy] = hist(T, M);
subplot(2,2,1),bar(yy,nn,'w'), xlabel('t'), ylabel('f(t)'),grid,...
        title(['Histogram for Weibull RVs with m = ',num2str(m),' & c =',num2str(c)])
[y,i]=hist(T,M);
Y=zeros(1,M);
Y = cumsum(y);
Y(M) = Y(M) - 1;
Y=Y./N;
subplot(2,2,2),plot(i,Y,'w'), xlabel('t'), ylabel('F(t)'), grid,...
        title('cdf histogram')
yy=log(-log(1-Y));
subplot(2,2,3),plot(log(i+.001),yy,'xw'), xlabel('i'),...
        ylabel('ln{-ln[1 - F(i)]}'), grid,...
        title('log-log data for fit')
p=polyfit(log(i+.0001),yy,1);
m_est = p(1);
c_est = exp(-p(2)/m_est);
f=polyval(p,log(i+.0001));
subplot(2,2,4),plot(log(i+.0001),f,'--w'), xlabel('i'),...
        ylabel('linear ms fit'), grid,...
        title(['Estimates for m = ', num2str(m_est),' & c = ', num2str(c_est)])
print c:\probab\compex\ce8_3 -dps

» ce8_3
Enter c parameter 30
Enter m parameter 35
Enter total random numbers to generate 5000
```

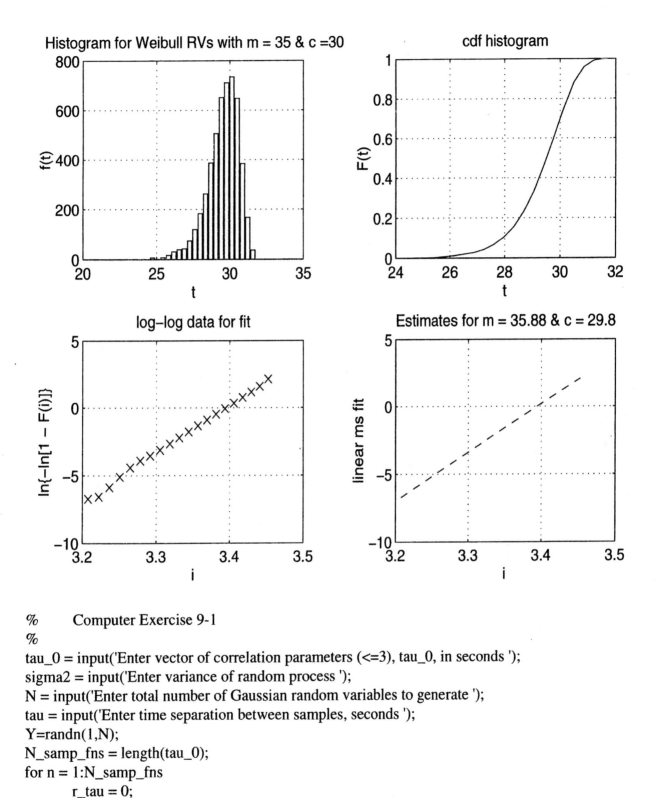

```
%        Computer Exercise 9-1
%
tau_0 = input('Enter vector of correlation parameters (<=3), tau_0, in seconds ');
sigma2 = input('Enter variance of random process ');
N = input('Enter total number of Gaussian random variables to generate ');
tau = input('Enter time separation between samples, seconds ');
Y=randn(1,N);
N_samp_fns = length(tau_0);
for n = 1:N_samp_fns
        r_tau = 0;
        if abs(tau) < tau_0(n)
                r_tau = 1 - abs(tau)/tau_0(n);
```

```
        end
        cond_var = sigma2*(1 - r_tau^2);
        X = zeros(size(Y));
        X(1) = Y(1);
        t = zeros(size(Y));
        for k = 2:N
                cond_mean = r_tau*Y(k-1);
                X(k) = sqrt(cond_var)*Y(k) + cond_mean;
                t(k) = (k-1)*tau;
        end
        subplot(3,1,n), plot(t, X),xlabel('Time, seconds'),...
        ylabel('Amplitude'),grid,axis([0 N*tau -3*sqrt(sigma2), 3*sqrt(sigma2)]),...
        title(['Sample of Gaussian random process for correl. between samples of
',num2str(r_tau)])
end
```

» ce9_1
Enter vector of correlation parameters (<=3), tau_0, in seconds [.1 .2 2]
Enter variance of random process 4
Enter total number of Gaussian random variables to generate 500
Enter time separation between samples, seconds .1

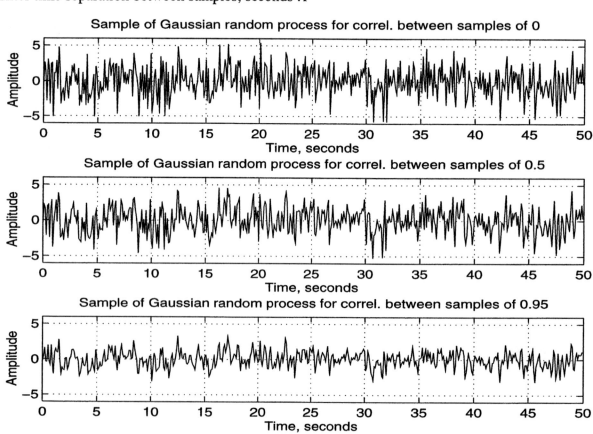

```
%         Computer Exercise 9-2
%
clg
beta_1v = input('Enter vector of values (total <= 4) for beta 1 (< 1) ');
beta_2v = input('Enter vector of values (total <= 4) for beta 2 (beta_1 + beta_2 <= 1) ');
sigma2 = input('Enter variance of random process ');
N = input('Enter total number of Gaussian random variables to generate ');
L1 = length(beta_1v);
L2 = length(beta_2v);
for l1 = 1:L1
for l2 = 1:L2
if l1==1
        l = l2;
        else
        l = 2+l2;
end
beta_1 = beta_1v(l1);
beta_2 = beta_2v(l2);
alpha = 1 - beta_1 - beta_2;
NN=sqrt(sigma2)*randn(1,N);
X = zeros(size(NN));
X(1) = 0;
X(2) = 0;
t = zeros(size(NN));
for k = 3:N
        X(k) = beta_1*X(k-1) + beta_2*X(k-2) + alpha*NN(k);
        t(k) = (k-1);
end
subplot(4,1,l),plot(t, X),xlabel('Sample number'),...
        ylabel('Amplitude'),grid,...
        title(['Sample function for beta1, beta2, variance = ', num2str(beta_1),', ',
num2str(beta_2),', ', num2str(sigma2)])
if l == 1
        hold on
end
end
end
```

» ce9_2
Enter vector of values (total <= 4) for beta 1 (< 1) [.1 .5]
Enter vector of values (total <= 4) for beta 2 (beta_1 + beta_2 <= 1) [.05 .45]
Enter variance of random process 4
Enter total number of Gaussian random variables to generate 100

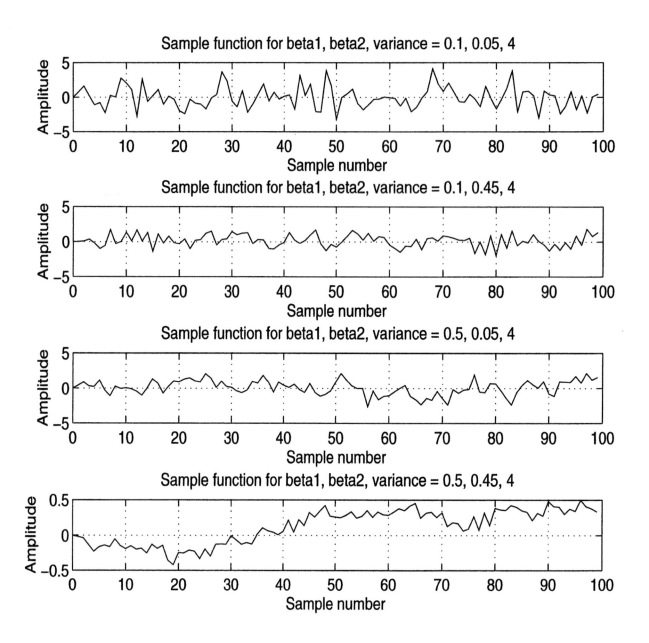

```
%        Computer exercise 10-1
%
clg
device = input('Enter 1 for dead zone device; 2 for limiter ');
N = input('Enter number of random variables to generate ');
M = input('Enter number of bins for histogram ');
if device == 1
        c = input('Enter break point normalized by std dev of input for dead zone device ');
elseif device == 2
```

```
            c = input('Enter limit level normalized by std dev of input for limiter ');
end
X = zeros(1,N);
Y = zeros(1,N);
t = zeros(1,N);
X = randn(1, N);
for k = 1:N
        t(k) = k-1;
        if device == 1
                if X(k) > -c & X(k) < c
                Y(k) = 0;
                elseif X(k) >= c
                Y(k) = X(k) - c;
                elseif X(k) <= -c
                Y(k) = X(k) + c;
                end
        elseif device == 2
                if X(k) <= c & X(k) >= -c
                Y(k) = X(k);
                elseif X(k) > c
                Y(k) = c;
                else
                Y(k) = -c;
                end
        end
end
[n,x] = hist(Y,M);
delta = x(2)-x(1);
if device == 1
subplot(311),bar(x, n/(N*delta),'-w'), grid, xlabel('output amplitude'),...
        ylabel('probability density'),...
        title(['Normalized histogram of dead zone device output; dead zone half-width = '
num2str(c)])
elseif device == 2
subplot(311),bar(x, n/(N*delta),'-w'), grid, xlabel('output amplitude'),...
        ylabel('probability density'),...
        title(['Normalized histogram of limiter output; limit level = ' num2str(c)])
end
subplot(312),plot(t,X,'w'),axis([0 500 -3 3]),grid,xlabel('sample number'),...
        ylabel('amplitude'),title('Input time series')
subplot(313),plot(t,Y,'w'),axis([0 500 -3 3]),grid,xlabel('sample number'),...
        ylabel('amplitude'),title('Output time series')
print c:\probab\compex\ce10_1a -dps
```

» ce10_1
Enter 1 for dead zone device; 2 for limiter 1
Enter number of random variables to generate 5000
Enter number of bins for histogram 21
Enter break point normalized by std dev of input for dead zone device 1
»
» ce10_1
Enter 1 for dead zone device; 2 for limiter 2
Enter number of random variables to generate 5000
Enter number of bins for histogram 21
Enter limit level normalized by std dev of input for limiter 2

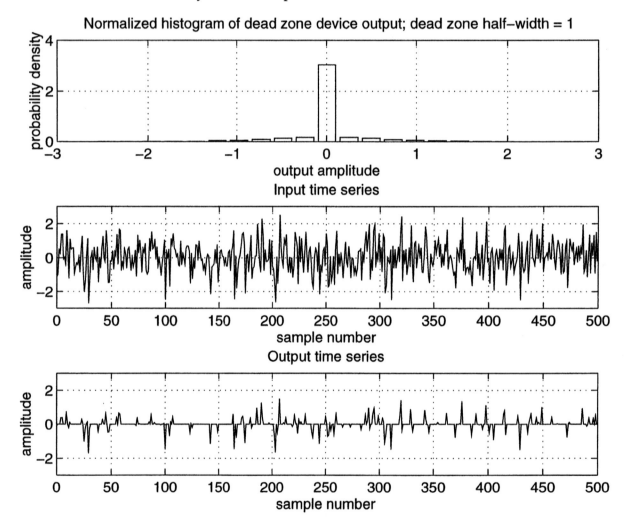

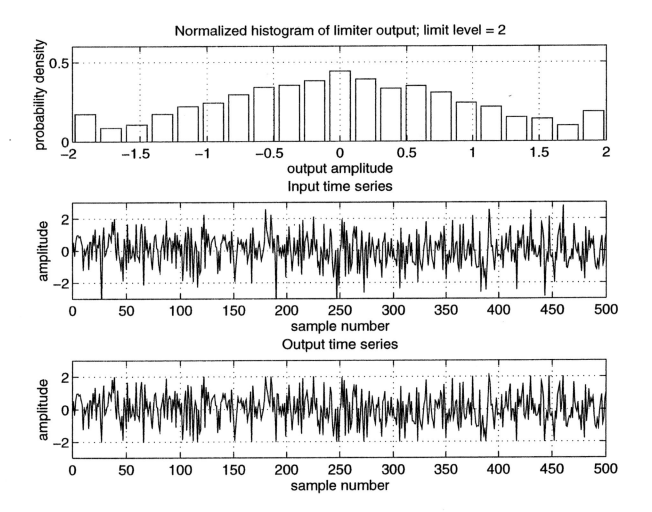

Normalized histogram of limiter output; limit level = 2

Input time series

Output time series

% Computer Exercise 10-2
%
N = input('Enter desired order of Butterworth filter ');
Ns = input('Enter number of Gaussian samples ');
for k = 1:3
  X = randn(1, Ns);
  Wn = 0.1*(2*k-1);
  [B,A] = butter(N,Wn);
  Y = filter(B, A, X);
  t = [0:1:length(Y)-1];
  subplot(3,1,k),plot(t, Y, '-w'),xlabel('t'),ylabel('Y(t)'),...
  title(['Gaussian sample function for filter of order ', num2str(N),' and bandwidth ',
num2str(Wn),' of a half sampling frequency'])
end

167

» ce10_2
Enter desired order of Butterworth filter 5
Enter number of Gaussian samples 500

Gaussian sample function for filter of order 5 and bandwidth 0.1 of a half sampling frequency

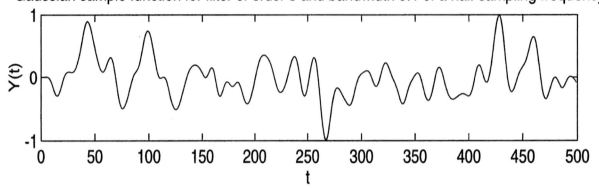

Gaussian sample function for filter of order 5 and bandwidth 0.3 of a half sampling frequency

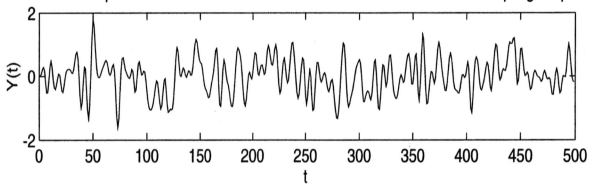

Gaussian sample function for filter of order 5 and bandwidth 0.5 of a half sampling frequency

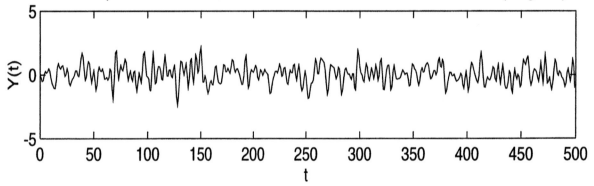

Errata - Solutions Manual for *Elements of Engineering Probability and Statistics*
by Rodger E. Ziemer

Page	Problem/line	Correction
4	line 6 from bottom	remove one of double parentheses on right
4	line 4 from bottom	insert 9 in { } for answer for (a); right side should be {0, 1, 2, 3, 4, 5, 6, 7, 8, 9}
6	line 1	answer (b) should be $P(B) = \frac{1}{2}$
6	line 5	$P(A \cap X)$ should be $P(B \cap X)$
6	line 6 from bottom	"Number of persons reading 1 paper only" should be "Number of persons reading at least 1 newspaper"
6	lines 1 & 2, bottom	right side of equation should read = 100,000 - 32,000 = 68,000
7	Prob. 2-12, left fig.	$X > Y$ should be $X < Y$
8	line 7 from top	0.125/0.0.5 should be 0.125/0.5
9	Prob. 2-20	2nd "box 1" should be "box 2" for all equations; 3rd "box 1" should be "box 3" for all equations
9	Prob. 2-20(a)	answer should be 43/216, not 7/216
9	Prob. 2-20(c)	answer should be 31/216, not 31/72
9	Prob. 2-21(c)	the 2/201 in last line should be 990/995
9	Prob. 2-22(b)	replace the 0.9 by 0.3
10	Prob. 2-24	answer to (b) should be 0.01 (the asked for probability should be $P(D \mid F)$
13	last equation	should be P(three aces)
17	line 5 in 2nd table	answer for $X = 9$ should be 0.2623; the following combinations were left out of the first table: rwb, brw, bwr, wrb, wbr
19	last equation	delete the $= Q(2^{1/2})$
21	last 2 lines	the notation should be $\lceil \; \rceil$
22	first 2 equations	should be $P(> 2$ errors)
22	1st and 3rd eq'ns	upper limits on sums should be 2, not 3
23	line 6 from bottom	$p(1 - p)^3$ should be $p(1 - p)^2$
25	3rd equation	the 2 in all exponents should be 3
28	Prob. 3-25, 1st eq.	equation needs to be below line currently below it
29	Prob. 3-27	answer should be 6/5 (the wrong value of $P(H)$ was substituted)

31	Prob. 3-29, 2nd eq.	denominator 12 should be 21
31	Prob. 3-29, part b	$E(Y) = 8/9$; $var(Y) = 6.123$
33	Prob. 3-31	answer should be $M_x = 9/(9 + v^2)$; $m_x = 0$; $m_2 = 2/9 = var(X)$ (the pdf is changed in the problem to $1.5 \exp(-3|x|)$
35	Prob. 3-34 (a)	the probability should be $\leq 1/2^2$
35	Prob. 3-34 (b)	answer is 0, not 1
36	Prob. 3-34 (c)	the actual probability is $e^{-3} = 0.0498 < 0.25$
36	Prob. 3-35 (b)	the probability is 0 (range of integration is outside the nonzero region of the pdf)
36	Prob. 3-35(c)	the probability is e^{-4}
43	Prob. 4-6, lines 1 & 2	60 should be 30; 75 should be 40; 50 should be 20; 70 should be 40
44	Prob. 4-8, 2nd int.	exponent v should have absolute value signs around it
46	Line 7 from bottom	change "chose" to "chosen"
53	2nd & 3rd equations	exponent of both should be $-z/2\sigma^2$ (remove square on z); last equation should have $1/2\sigma^2$ multiplying expontial (remove z)
56	Prob. 5-2	Same as the solution to Prob. 6-6
65	Lines 2 and 4	reference should be to (5-32), not (5-30)
72	last equation	insert a b after 6-22 in the subscript on right hand side
73	first equation	insert a b after 6-22 in the subscript on right hand side
76	line 4	reference should be to Example 6-6, not Example 6-5
77	line 6	reference should be to Example 6-8, not Example 6-7
95	lines 5 & 6, bottom	"slope 2" and "slope -2", respectively, not "slope 1" and "slope -1"
97	last equation	change the -1 to $\sin(2\omega_0 t)$
98	2nd line of equation	change t to τ in first cos; take out the factor of 2 in front of $2\omega_0\tau$ in the 2nd cos
98	3rd & 4th lines of eq.	take out the factor of 2 in front of the $2\omega_0\tau$ (3 places)
98	5th & 6th lines of eq.	change $2\omega_0(t + \tau)$ to $2\omega_0 t + \omega_0\tau$ (3 places)
103	line above last eq	remove the subscript Z from σ_z^2
107	Prob. 10-2, 2nd line	reference to (9-54) should be to (9-57)